Beyond Pearl Harbor
I Company in the Pacific of WWII

Henry C. Zabierek

BURD STREET PRESS
SHIPPENSBURG, PENNSYLVANIA

Front Cover: "Men of the 7th Division using flame throwers to smoke out Japs from a block house on Kwajalein Island, while others wait with rifles ready in case Japs come out." Cordray, February 4, 1944. 111-SC-212770, National Archives

Back Cover: "Army reinforcements disembarking from LST's Form a graceful curve as they proceed across coral reef toward the beach." Laudansky, Saipan, ca. June/July 1944. 111-SC-191475, National Archives

The acid-free paper used in this book meets the guidelines for permanence and durability of the Committee on Production Guidelines for Book Longevity of the Council on Library Resources.

For a complete list of available publications
please write
Burd Street Press
Division of White Mane Publishing Company, Inc.
P.O. Box 708
Shippensburg, PA 17257-0708 USA

Library of Congress Cataloging-in-Publication Data

Zabierek, Henry C., 1924-2008.
  Beyond Pearl Harbor : I Company in the Pacific of WWII / Henry C. Zabierek.
    p. cm.
  ISBN 978-1-57249-401-5 (pbk. : alk. paper)
  1. United States. Army. Infantry Regiment, 127th. Battalion, 3rd. Company I.
2. World War, 1939-1945--Regimental histories--United States. 3. World War, 1939-1945--Personal narratives, American. 4. World War, 1939-1945--Campaigns--Pacific Region. 5. Zabierek, Henry C., 1924-2008. I. Title.

  D769.31127th .Z33 2010
  940.54'1273--dc22

                                                          2010001436

Contents

Foreword

No history of World War II would be complete without the story of the war in the Pacific. Largely a stepchild to the main action in Europe for most of the war, the Pacific War was begun with outdated weapons and fewer resources in manpower and firepower. It was fought in places then unknown and since easily forgotten.

The Pacific War was fought on a smaller scope than its European counterpart. Jungle terrain limited actions to a smaller unit perspective, such as the company, the platoon, or squad level. Troop advances were measured in yards, not miles. The searing heat, the greater threat of disease, the presence of trails but not roads, and the totally alien nature of the enemy combined for obstacles greater than found in the European Theater of Operations.

The training of troops for battle had been done with Europe in mind. For the Pacific, that meant troops would learn by doing. As casualties mounted, more and more replacements filled the ranks. The newcomers arrived from a variety of sources and levels of training. Some had never fired a weapon before and were unacquainted with the gun provided them. There was no time for hands-on training. Rookies who had been told "You'll learn," sometimes perished before they did.

Beyond Pearl Harbor: I Company in the Pacific of WWII chronicles the actual incidents and battles that illustrate the nature of the Pacific War. From the earliest days of the campaign in New Guinea to the eventual occupation of Japan, the peculiar nature of the fighting in the Southwest Pacific is played out. The close proximity of the combatants, the incremental advances, the occasional retreats, the frequent banzai attacks, and the unorthodox strategy and tactics of the enemy are all in evidence as the company moves closer to the eventual, but sudden victory.

Chapter 1

THE QUESTIONER

"When are we going to be relieved?"

The question pierced the jet-black darkness of the New Guinea night. It heightened the attention of even the drowsiest soldier on guard duty in the foxholes along the I Company perimeter. Some of these men had joined the company that very afternoon. They were unfamiliar with the guns they toted. They knew not yet the experience of shooting and being shot at. They were ill prepared for handling the situation that had been presented. None of their previous training had prepared them for the war they would have to fight. More experienced heads were needed to prevent any rash action.

Manny Rockwell, the platoon sergeant, passed the word. Up and down the company's line, the same stark orders were repeated: "Don't fire unless someone lays a hand on you."

Rockwell was stalling for time while he figured out both what had just happened and what, if anything, should be done about it. Who asked the question? Why? Was it a coincidence that the word "relieved" served as part of the company's password that night?

Rockwell was a veteran of almost a year of fighting in the New Guinea jungle. He knew firsthand of Japanese trickery and actions that Americans saw as unconventional and irrational. Only a week ago, he had killed an enemy soldier who had tunneled into I Company lines. Now he wondered if he had heard correctly. After all, each night's password contained the letter "l" because of the enemy's difficulty in pronouncing that letter. Had he heard something like "rerieved"?

Rockwell passed further instructions. "Keep listening. Wait for further orders."

Rockwell's company had established their defensive perimeter only days ago. His men were exhausted from a period of intense fighting, some of it hand-to-hand. The enemy was frantic to drive Americans into the sea from the tip of New Guinea. Today New Guinea, tomorrow Australia. A nighttime banzai attack brought horrendous loss of life to the Japanese. Though the company's losses were dramatically fewer, Rockwell and Captain Leonard, the company commander, were forced to stop, regroup, and take on replacements. Now they preferred no gun battles unless there was an attack.

Rockwell thought of his squad leaders. Given the number of replacements that were being added to the platoon, they would have to acquaint the rookies with the niceties of combat conditions overnight. They needed to be leaders more than in name.

J. C. Pickens was a remarkably carefree veteran and the unofficial storyteller of the platoon. By now his stories had been told so often that his buddies corrected him on details as Pickens told the story yet another time. Imaginary or real, his stories concerned his "Daddy" and their shooting of birds in his native South Carolina. But Pickens knew when to be serious, and he was cool and effective when the going got rough.

Rex Akers loved a good time, but New Guinea was not an ideal place to enjoy one. His soft Georgia accent revealed his southern roots. His laugh was infectious, and was often heard when safety permitted. But Akers could return to the seriousness that was demanded almost immediately. He demanded much of his squad, chewed them out when they did stupid things, and always led by example. Sergeant Akers led from the front.

Pete Kowalsky of Indiana was dubbed "The Professor," once it was known he had completed a year of college. On the surface, he seemed out of place as an infantry squad leader. He was better educated than any others in the platoon. He mentioned books that were totally foreign to those whose only books were of the comic variety. Kowalsky was no student of war, though stories of his toughness in battle were well known among the entire platoon. Rockwell admired him, though Kowalsky was unafraid to question his decisions. And, on more than one occasion, their words were heated and not fit for publication. But Kowalsky was loyal when it counted and his platoon leader counted heavily upon him.

The night wore on. By now Rockwell wondered if he had heard correctly. And then he wondered if he had heard anything at all.

If this were an enemy intruder, he hoped that someone would not react and reveal the exact location of the platoon. With so many in the outfit not yet baptized by fire, there was danger of a shot being fired recklessly. Rockwell felt compelled to spread the word along the lines once again to react only when attacked. So far, the warning was holding.

Rockwell now sought sleep. He had been robbed of it. Within hours, the unmatched darkness of the New Guinea night would give way to dawn. Another day of danger would begin. Rest was precious.

And then it came. It was louder and nearer than before.

"When are we going to be rerieved?"

It was unmistakable. There was an enemy intruder. And the direction and distance of his whereabouts were much more obvious.

Rockwell enlisted the help of two of the new arrivals. "Follow my directions like your life depended on it because it does. Take a grenade, pull the pin, and hold the handle down. Now, when I say 'go', let the handle up, count to two and throw it about thirty feet in that direction."

The grenades went menacingly on their way. A flash and deafening explosions followed. Limbs of trees shattered like matchsticks. Shrapnel rained down over a wide area. It had been so silent, and now the ugly sounds of war had returned.

The silence resumed. The light of day would reveal that the grenades had accomplished their deadly mission. The questioner would ask no more questions.

Chapter 2

THE ATTACK

It seemed incredible. It had to be impossible. It could not be.

For over a week, I Company had sent daily patrols across the river to check on possible enemy activity. The patrols often included some of the latest replacements, if only to acquaint them with front line life. The incursions over the river usually penetrated as much as a mile inland, yet they encountered no sign of enemy activity. Thus, while the company remained alert, no immediate enemy action seemed possible.

In a wink, any such assurances were dashed. The enemy came at the midnight hour, seemingly in hordes. Flares over the river preceded their advance and the river was lighted with the clarity of a modern baseball stadium. Some dragged their artillery pieces across the one hundred yard expanse of the shallow river. For battle veterans, this was another case of the enemy doing the unanticipated. For the newly arrived this was war, Pacific style.

Chaos reigned within I Company. Panic ensued for some as they fired their rifles indiscriminately. Enemy mortar shells squealed as they leveled trees on their way to further destruction. Bullets seemingly filled the air. Word of company dead added to the tension. They included Owens, Scalani, Repulski, Petrovich, and MacPhee. It threatened to become a slaughterhouse.

Captain Leonard sent word through Rockwell that machine gunners should continue their steady fire, even as the barrels approached a white-hot stage. Mortar gunners were ordered to pound the attackers. Riflemen were on guard for enemy infiltrators. The attack along the entire perimeter must be repulsed at all cost.

Some order was restored among company ranks, if only temporarily. Machine guns and mortars were proving to be effective, as the enemy dead seen on the rocks in the river could attest. The Japanese seemed to accommodate the Americans by charging straight into their guns. But the attack continued with steady intensity, though the brunt of the attack veered to the left.

It was apparent that the enemy sought a soft spot in the lines in order to make a breakthrough. They found it in the M Company lines. The enemy stormed through by the hundreds and raced forward, inflicting lethal damage on the company. The worst possible situation now confronted I Company. Enemy troops were now in front and behind them. I Company was in danger of being cut off.

One enemy infantryman crawled straight toward newcomer Hamilton, who shot at him and missed. The enemy soldier did not miss. Hamilton plunged face down in a puddle of blood. The enemy's own stay was but for an instant. A burst of machine gun fire severed his head from his body.

Uncertainty reigned in the I Company ranks. Now every noise was suspect and anyone who appeared on the trail was a potential enemy. The damage from friendly fire became a possibility. The danger was greatest among the newly arrived, who might shoot out of fear.

Fortunately, calm and decisiveness prevailed at the company command level. Captain Leonard was held in awe by his men. His many actions of bravery were legendary. He was no stranger to the front lines. He had their respect. They would carry out his orders no matter what the peril.

Leonard's reputation was put to the test. Of all things, he ordered a withdrawal to the rear. No one would question it, though neither Leonard nor his men knew what they would encounter. A full moon shed light on what would otherwise have been the unmatched darkness of a New Guinea night. Orders were passed to maintain silence in order not to reveal their whereabouts. The retreat began.

July was always a wet month in this part of New Guinea. The rain was never light; it was torrential. No matter what the discomfort, there were more lethal things to fear. Though the terrain was level, swamps were ever-present. Noise came only from the splashing of the water and the sucking sounds of boots pulling out of the mud, but nary a sound from the men. The march was funereal.

Miraculously, although rifle fire and machine fire were expected, none came. Conditions remained miserable and the fording of streams was challenging. But anything, even the miseries of the jungle, was preferred to enemy fire.

The troops slogged on, unmindful of time. Finally, the company was halted near a slight rise in the terrain. Leonard ordered that a perimeter be set up. Rockwell passed the word that the silence be maintained.

Daybreak arrived in quiet, but all too soon. Eat they must, even though the K Rations were seen by some as punishment, and not nourishment. No fire was possible to heat the hash or the water for the instant coffee. The wet conditions made the crackers soggy. Even though the cigarettes were dry, they could not be smoked because they might give away their locale to the enemy. The situation was miserable but hey, they weren't being fired upon.

Now Captain Leonard's orders seemed incredible. After just having withdrawn for about two miles, the order now was to retrace those steps and return to their original perimeter along the river! Any enemy that were encountered were to be destroyed. Coming from any other commander, these orders would have been questioned.

The return march would not be without incident. The silence that had prevailed was shattered as soon as the first swamp had to be crossed. The chattering of machine guns started sporadically, then became more intense.

Leonard ordered the men to seek cover, while he pondered his next move. Was this a token enemy force, left behind to harass and inflict casualties? Or was this a full-fledged unit?

The company commander sent for Rockwell as he sought to make a successful return to the river with the least loss of life. They had already suffered too large a death toll during the river attack.

"We've got to find out how large this outfit is that's attacking us," Leonard began. "The machine guns seem to be set up on the ridge to the left. How many of these there are and how large the force accompanying them is anyone's guess. But we've got to be sure."

Rockwell dared to interject. "My guess is that this is a skeleton crew. They waited until we were vulnerable crossing the swamp before they opened up. A larger force would not have allowed us to get to this point."

Leonard had already reached the same conclusion. "We've got to get a patrol out to find out where the gunners are and how big the force is. Have one of your squad leaders form a patrol. Send a machine gun along. Meanwhile, have your mortar men ready."

Akers would lead the patrol. His instructions were simple. He was to proceed to the left, reach the ridge, and establish contact.

He wasted no time. He gave the three rookie patrol members a crash course in survival. "Make as little noise as possible. Have your weapons ready. Drop to the ground at the first shot. Wait for orders. Don't get yourselves killed. We need you."

Out of the mire of the swamp, the terrain seemed ideal by comparison. The rookies seemed to be in a state of both wonderment and fear. The veterans did not wonder; they only feared.

After about twenty minutes, Akers stopped the patrol. They had reached the ridge without incident. "We can't be very far from where the firing was coming from," he told the men. "When we make contact, follow orders."

His words came none too soon. A burst of enemy machine-gun fire breached the silence. "Down," he screeched, amid the din. It proved to be too late for newcomer Tempkin. Hit in the neck, he died without a murmur. Fortunately, the rest of the patrol found themselves in a hollow. Enemy machine guns fired over their heads. Luckily, Akers was situated behind a large tree. Using it as a shield, he peered around to survey the situation. Gradually, two machine gun nests that were partially camouflaged could be seen. Since they were near the end of the ridge, Akers concluded that there were no more such nests.

Akers ordered a withdrawal. The mission had been accomplished. Loss of life was expected, but never accepted. Death never became routine. A contingent would be sent to retrieve Tempkin's body. His war had lasted less than a week.

Because of the hollow and thick jungle cover, the rest of the patrol was able to return unscathed. Akers delivered his findings to Leonard and Rockwell.

Leonard reached his decision swiftly. "Let's use the mortars to knock out those damned guns. Have them fire as many smoke shells as needed to zero in on where the machine guns seem to be. Then fire five rounds from all four guns."

Rockwell delivered the message. The mortar men sprang into action. Smoke clouded the ridge as the first shells landed. The crew was certain that they were on target. Five rounds from four guns boomed on their way.

Leonard did no wait for the smoke to clear. The company renewed its advance, however warily. Quiet ensued. The machine guns had been silenced, either temporarily or permanently.

The lull in the action was short-lived. Predictably, trouble occurred as the men began traversing another swamp. This time Leonard was defiant. He ordered small arms fire on the enemy machine gunners. A toll on the enemy was extracted and I Company would report the deaths of Lewis and Maroni, with three others injured. The contingent proceeded.

Further obstacles were encountered. It was now clear that the enemy action was more harassment than all-out attack. Nonetheless, they extracted a price. Five men had been killed and a like number were being borne on stretchers by native tribesmen. While the losses were not surprising, they were devastating. More replacements would be needed. The cycle kept repeating.

The return was completed by late afternoon. The men seemed dazed by the changing fortunes of the last few days. Had they had the time for retrospection, they would have realized that the events of recent days were the stuff of miracles. They had withdrawn in defeat, fear, confusion, and almost certain disaster. They suffered damage, but not disaster. Leonard's plan began as daring, and ended as the work of genius. Most important, the company was sustained by its successful return.

Now that they had returned to their positions on the river, they again would be the attackers. Now they would cross the river. More and bitter battles lay ahead. For now, it was enough that they were spared to fight them.

Chapter 3

THE HILL

The mission assigned to I Company and the 3rd Battalion was all too familiar. Nothing was omitted. The task was "to destroy all installations, annihilate the enemy, and capture and retain the ground held by the Japanese."

"This is typical army," laughed Sergeant Rockwell. "Is there anything that was left out?"

His veterans of the jungles of New Guinea had expected more open terrain in the Philippines. They had heard of the Leyte and Ormoc Valleys, sometimes fifteen miles in width. They anticipated fighting in the open, and the chances to advance more quickly.

The topography of Leyte where I Company was to fight differed little from what they had known. Not only was there jungle, but it was mostly mountainous. Swamps and streams posed hazards. What roads existed were poor. It was as if they had never left New Guinea.

The enemy was determined that the Americans would not wrest Leyte from them. The elite of their forces were brought in. Every means were to be employed to defend against and repel the invaders. Banzai attacks, infiltration, and various suicide missions would be the norm, not the exception.

The importance of the Hill could not be overemphasized. Possession of the Hill meant control of all the surrounding area. It was the commanding position on the road to Ormoc, located on the other side of the island. It was strategically crucial. There could be no capture of Leyte without control of the Hill.

Rockwell gathered his squad leaders. The mood was somber.

"None of this is going to be pretty," he began. "We've got some rookies who have never fired the gun they are carrying. They've never been tested under fire."

"They may be the lucky ones," said Akers, in his recognizable southern drawl. "They don't know how tough the days ahead may be. They're not as scared as the rest of us."

Pickens knew that this would be much tougher than shooting squirrels in his native South Carolina. "The longer you're in this damned war, the more chance you have of getting hit. You just gotta figure that if your number is up, that's it. There's nothing you can do about it."

Kowalsky, ever serious and scholarly looking, urged caution. "We've got to get these guys ready without frightening them. They're going to lose some of their newly-found friends. They're going to learn that war is about killing. There is a chance that some may want to break and run. We may bend at times, but we can't break."

Rockwell turned to specifics. "Captain Leonard has it all laid out for us. He's remarkable in tough situations. He knows the days ahead will be rough, but he has no doubt that we will take this hill. We're going to be in the center of the lines. L Company will be on our left, and K Company will be on our right. It is important that we leave no opening between us."

After hearing the details, Akers felt they sounded all too familiar. "This really sounds like New Guinea all over again," he began. "We're still in a jungle. We're going to be dealing with small arms, machine guns, and mortars. Any gains we make will be in yards, not miles."

"Yeah, this looks even tougher than we've known before," countered Pickens. "These birds have been crazy before. Now they'll be even nuttier."

Kowalsky gathered his squad. He went through the details of what they were to do. The mood was somber, yet purposeful. There was no problem with attention. Soldiers don't like to die.

Then Kowalsky got to particulars. "We have our orders. Take his damned hill. The enemy will fight to the last man. These are the best troops they have. They cannot afford to lose Leyte. They have had plenty of time to dig in and zero their guns on key areas. They will be in pill-boxes, caves, machine gun nests, and even roots of trees. It will seem like they're everywhere.

"You've got to be smart. Dumb guys don't last. Move fast when you're in the open and crouch low. Don't stand still. Never relax your guard. Expect everything, like banzai attacks. You will never hear such noise in your life. Your job is to kill every last one of them.

"Remember, they said we couldn't land here. Then they said we'd quit, once we saw our buddies killed. Well, we've lost some good friends. And now we're going to kill the bastards that killed our friends.

"Captain Leonard knows we can take this hill. He's a tough son-of-a-bitch. He's already been wounded three times, but that doesn't stop him. Just yesterday, while he was pointing out our position, he shot a Jap and took him prisoner. Two guys took him away on a stretcher. A short time later, the men returned with an empty stretcher. They said he tried to escape."

There were no dramatic flourishes to launch the attack. No bells were sounded, no starter's gun fired into the air, and no horns tooted. With a mere wave of the arm, Rockwell's company moved forward. Progress, even without enemy opposition, was slow. The terrain was uneven and the underbrush was heavy.

Although the men had been told to expect fierce and fanatical opposition, only scattered fighting was anticipated in the early going. The troops followed instructions, exposed themselves little, and inched forward. Things seemed to be moving on cue.

Not for long. So much for predictability. In what seemed only a flash, enemy rifle fire filled the air. Their machine guns then chattered their deadly melody. Mortar shells whined before inflicting their damage. The carnage was immediate. Wilson and Callahan appeared to be the first victims. Rivers was hit so badly that he would lose both legs. Raditz moaned, an arm almost totally severed. "The bastards," muttered Rockwell, as he crouched and crawled among the men, ensuring they would hold their positions.

The din remained deafening. Enemy rifle and machine gun fire seemed relentless. Rockwell's men ducked in unison when the whine of mortar shells was heard. The company was pinned down. The first day was threatening to become a bloodbath.

Captain Leonard called for more mortar fire. The troops took heart as the outgoing shells whizzed overhead. He dared not ask for artillery fire, given the closeness of the fighting. Enemy targets were only being guessed at. The entrenched enemy seemed to be everywhere, but they could be seen nowhere.

Leonard now faced a dilemma. It would be a near disaster to withdraw on the first day of the attack. Yet it was clear that this was one of the worst days of the war for the company. In truth, there was only one choice. The company must live to fight another day. Leonard called for smoke shells in order to shroud the troops in their withdrawal. The battered, shell-shocked soldiers withdrew as swiftly as they could manage. It was not a proud day. Now a new battle plan was needed.

The company tried to regroup after its very bad day. Its numbers were fewer. Rookies had become veterans in one day. War was neither glamorous nor painless. It was about killing. Worse still, there seemed no end in sight.

Stories of near misses and close calls abounded. Wallace had a bullet pierce his helmet, go around and around, then drop out without a scratch on him. Alveni's shovel had its handle shot off. Lemon was unscathed after having a hole shot in his canteen. Captain Leonard's field radio was riddled with machine gun fire and ruined. War makes no exception for rank.

Even amid the savagery of the fighting, there was time for reflection and thankfulness. Oakes began it all. "Can you imagine what we'd do without these natives?"

"Yeah," said Kelly, referring to the native tribesmen, "these little rascals can do anything."

"What's amazing is how they seem to keep the stretchers level at all times, even though they're coming down steep terrain."

"There seems to be nothing they can't do. They lug rations, ammo, and even the mail."

"They go to places where no vehicle could ever get to."

"And they're such gutsy sons-of-guns. They go where the going is toughest. They pick up our guys in the middle of the action. They seem to have no fear."

Oakes laughed. "Remember what they told us before we came up here? They warned us to beware of savage headhunters! Maybe they should have told us about these damned Japs."

Leonard huddled with Rockwell. "We need to put more fire on them. We were like sitting ducks today. I'm going to call headquarters for artillery, and our own mortar guys are going to have a busy day. The enemy will learn that we may withdraw at times, but we aren't running away. We aren't going to capture this hill in a day. It may take a week or more. And we're going to kill a lot of Japs before we're through."

The night passed without incident. Guard duty took on more meaning as the men sought sleep between watches. The enemy inaction may have been due to the belief that the American withdrawal was permanent. After all, they had inflicted what one GI called a "living hell" on him and his buddies.

However, the men now realized that all nights that would follow might not be like this. War follows no predictable schedule. It is not founded on convenience. And the enemy in this case was a master of deception and unpredictability.

The American shelling began at dawn. For the moment, at least, the shells were headed in the right direction. The artillery used their 105's and their more powerful 155's. In addition, the company 60- and 81-millimeter mortars pumped out their deadly fare.

Pickens passed among his squad, alternately encouraging, counseling, and warning. "We can't keep going backwards. They think we're going to give up. Forget it. We need that hill and we're going to get it. Now let's kill all the bastards we can."

The company pushed off for the second day. The opposition began immediately. Rockwell spotted an enemy machine gun nest. He ordered a temporary halt, while he phoned for mortar fire. The first smoke shells landed beyond the machine gun emplacement. Rockwell advised the gunners of the necessary target corrections. Happily, the next round landed on target. Some of Pickens' men stormed the machine gun nest. Four of the enemy emerged and sought escape. They were riddled with an avenging hail of bullets. The machine gun had been silenced. The company was coming of age.

The troops moved on. Suddenly, more than a score of Japanese charged Akers' squad. They waved their arms and shouted the word that chilled the most hardy of the invaders. "Banzai!" filled the air. It was the dreaded real thing. Most of the enemy had guns, but some who led did not. They would sacrifice themselves so that others could break through.

"Don't stop firing," shouted Akers in the midst of the din. "We can't let them through."

The carnage for the enemy was immense. Bodies began to pile up on bodies. But the sheer numbers allowed some to reach into the company lines. Desperate fighting followed, much of it on instinct.

Rockwell was not spared. Hardly had he risen to throw yet another grenade, when an enemy soldier charged him. Up close he was the caricature of the fire-breathing damned Jap that Rockwell had been taught to hate. He seemed to be the propaganda poster boy: round bodied, thick glasses, and bucktoothed. A bayonet on his rifle, he lunged straight at Rockwell's chest. Rockwell ducked, and the attacker tripped over him. His gun not in position to fire, Rockwell instinctively hammered the butt of his rifle to his adversary's skull over and over. Still shaking with fear, Rockwell pumped several shells into the dead man for good measure.

Rockwell had no time to reflect upon his closest brush with death. Only much later could he recall any particulars. For the moment, he wiped the dead man's blood from his rifle. The ultimate goal of war is to survive, whatever it takes.

The onslaught was over in an hour. The barrels of I Company's machine guns remained red hot. Rifles had been fired at rates unknown before. The company's numbers had dwindled, each squad losing men. Replacements were needed. But hope had been rekindled. Pickens was right. They were going to get that damned hill.

The company moved forward warily. Now some of the results of the shelling and small arms fire could be seen. Enemy bodies sometimes lay in grotesque positions. Parts of bodies lay apart from the torso. It was a grim scene of utter carnage that at other times would evoke revulsion, compassion, and pity.

But I Company had compassion only for its own. They had been taught to hate and had learned their lessons well. Those bastards were out to kill them and they must be killed first. They were not looked upon as fun-loving teenagers, fathers of families, or potential doctors. They were goddamned Japs. Remember Pearl Harbor.

It was only noon, but it seemed like midnight. Enough had occurred that morning to fill a lifetime of stories. The forward movement was incremental.

While Rockwell had urged caution, he emphasized urgency. The Hill had to be taken, but their foe was the best they had encountered. The insignia found on enemy bodies was that of the elite Japanese First Division. It was its general who vowed, "Leyte must not be taken."

The defenders tried to maximize their many advantages. They knew the territory. They had had the time to create elaborate strongholds. Every cave, every bunker, and even every tree root had to be contested. This was not a peaceful countryside.

By now I Company had developed a mode of attack against the enemy strongholds. Once discovered, the enemy was subjected to steady machine gun fire. While they were thus occupied, their positions were encircled. Grenades were lobbed into the holes, and then the attackers charged. It was not always done without casualties, but it proved to be effective. Each of the squads were to obliterate position that afternoon. It wasn't easy, but they were moving in the right direction.

First the whistle, then the "wham." The enemy was responding with their own mortar attack. "Medic!" yelled Davidson as the first of the dreaded mortar shells hit. Fortunately, most of the shells were falling short. The enemy seemed to be establishing the proper range.

Captain Leonard anticipated the enemy strategy and ordered a withdrawal. Advancement under such conditions would be suicidal. Buoyed as they were at escaping harm's way, the troops were dismayed at passing the territory that had just been so hard earned. Press forward, fall back. That is not what they had learned in basic training.

Pickens' squad began establishing a defensive perimeter. No one had to order the digging of foxholes. Mortar shells could do damage enough without inviting it. And the loss of some of their buddies was a sobering reminder that the prospect of death was real, and more so for the careless.

Pickens added the names of Moore and Jankowitz to the list of newly dead. The wounded had been evacuated to the aid station. But one GI was missing. Where was Joe Kramer?

Joe Kramer was a hulking, happy-go-lucky football player from Scranton, in territory where such games were a religion. The war had probably interrupted what would have been a lifetime in the coalmines for him. During the fighting, he gave "mean" new meaning. He had volunteered to wipe out an enemy machine gun nest that day. He had lobbed two grenades into the opening and flushed out three shell-shocked defenders. He helped to gun down all three as they tried to flee in panic. Kramer in action was a fighter possessed.

But where was he? He had not been seen since the attack on the nest. He was not among the body bags or the stretchers. None of the men could account for him. For the moment, at least, Kramer was missing in action.

As expected, the night did not pass without incident. Three of the enemy infiltrated the perimeter where Kowalsky's squad was situated. One foxhole had been unprotected. McMullan had fallen asleep on guard duty and now was never to awake. All three of the intruders were eliminated in a volley of bullets. Three for one. Invariably, some squad member would call this a "lousy trade."

The usual morning shelling preceded the company's advance. As it moved forward, there was ample evidence that the mortars had done their intended damage. It seemed that the enemy had planned its own attack. The tables had been turned. Those famous for the unpredictable were now the victims of it.

Surprisingly, the advance moved without untoward incident. Now the territory was familiar. They had been there a day ago. They revisited caves, bunkers, and tree roots to ensure their vacancy. The territory surrendered yesterday had been regained.

Pickens' squad neared the base of a small hill. The silence of enemy guns was welcome, but unnerving at the same time. Where were the defenders of Leyte? Wasn't it only yesterday when the fighting had been fierce here? Were they walking into a trap?

"What the hell is that?" The question came from Murphy of Pickens' squad. "What is that up on the side of the hill? It looks like a statue."

Pickens reached for his field glasses. He spotted the object of Murphy's inquiry. It was some sort of structure. A body had been propped in front of it. Pickens had never heard of Paul Bunyan. The size of the body evoked memories of the fabled woodcutter.

But Pickens needed no memories or folk tales to unravel the mystery. Dead bodies exposed to the searing heat bloated to abnormal size very quickly. The dead body was already larger than life.

"The bastards," muttered Pickens. "It's got to be Kramer. They've killed him. They're tempting us to come for the body. I'll radio Rockwell. Before we get our hides shot off, we need to send some shells in there."

Prior to any artillery or mortar shelling of the enemy, their exact location had to be determined. Had they left Kramer behind as they withdrew to higher ground? Or were they lurking nearby, eager to drag another hapless attacker into their bunker to repeat their hateful torture? Mere thought of the latter fueled the squad's thirst for revenge. Some were eager to storm the position, no matter what the cost.

An observation plane appeared, its mission to determine the enemy whereabouts. Back and forth it droned, seemingly stopping in mid air at times. The enemy could only regard this flight to nowhere as torturous, since they were the intended targets. By now the plane seemed to taunt them. It all proved to be too much. Rifle fire erupted, aimed at the plane. Some of the vaunted discipline of the defenders had come undone. Their position had been revealed. Now the barrage could begin.

The booming and whistling of the shells were welcome sounds as long as they were outgoing. No company grunt ever considered that this might be inhuman. None of them were alarmed at the prospect of bodies being blown apart. Hate left no opening for compassion. The object of war was victory, as so many generals claimed to be the first to say.

The company pushed off. For Pickens' squad there was only one immediate goal. They advanced cautiously for, despite the intensity of the shells rained upon them, the enemy's ability to withstand such onslaughts was legendary. Shell holes dotted the landscape. Some of the brush and tree cover had been leveled, exposing the company's men to easier detection.

Enemy gunfire erupted. Rifle shots followed. Damn the shelling, they had lived to fight another day. Heroes? Fanatics? It would depend on which side you asked. But there was no debate about their resilience. Leyte must not be taken.

Pickens peered through his field glasses again. "It can only be Kramer. And some of the machine gun fire seems to be coming from that area. If we're going to get him, we'll have to fight for him." Then he spat in the direction of the torturers.

Many volunteers came forward to begin the encirclement. Extreme caution was used, given the possibility of booby traps. Grenades were thrown at the entrance of the cave. Unintelligible voices came from within. As many as seven enemy soldiers emerged to run for cover. Some came out with guns firing, if only to cover for others. No one escaped. Company anger had been translated into expert marksmanship.

Now they turned to the sordid business of recovering their buddy's body. "God," was all that Harper could manifest as he choked back sobs. Fighting men do cry. There was compassion among the cruelty, yet it was reserved for their own.

A close-up view of Kramer revealed that his body had bloated grotesquely. Maggots had begun to do their dastardly deeds. On further examination, there were signs of torture and stab wounds on Kramer's body. It looked as if Kramer had died slowly, painfully, and cruelly. "Those miserable, goddamned, lousy, rotten bastards," was the best anyone could offer. It was so inadequate.

The native bearers came for the body. Older men might provoke wars, but young men fight them. Sometimes they die. The successful, prosperous future promised at Kramer's high school graduation must not have had him in mind. So much for oratory. Kramer was dead at nineteen. He had no future on earth.

The men thought of their own mortality. As much as death, they feared capture. Even though they were in the midst of fighting for their lives and witnessing and inflicting death at every turn, it was the Kramer experience that shook them. They knew of the horrors of Bataan and heard rumors of brutalities elsewhere, but that was far away. Kramer was not only close; Kramer was real.

Among the bandoliers of ammunition strewn across their chests, there was one other constant. In the center of the bullets was a grenade. No one ever instructed them to carry it. None of them discussed openly why they did so. However, everyone knew what no one said. If capture by the enemy seemed imminent, they would subvert it.

By now, one day seemed to blend into another. First the shelling, then the advance, another bunker or machine gun nest, a suicidal attack, attempted infiltration of the perimeter at night, and always a steady hail of rifle bullets. Only the intensity seemed to increase; the enemy was determined to retain Leyte.

There was also a sameness in other ways. Men couldn't remember whether they had eaten or not. Change of clothes was unthinkable. A bath was not within memory. If anyone had noticed, the heat was torrid. Yet all these things lacked real importance. Killing doesn't allow for distractions.

On the next day, Kowalsky's squad crossed a partially overgrown road and climbed to higher ground. Presently they heard a noise that was different from the crack of rifles and the chatter of machine guns. It sounded like a vehicle of some kind. But what? The road was not much more than a trail.

Squadretti spotted it first. It was adorned with brush, so as to camouflage its identity. Strangely, it looked like a moving forest. Of all things, it was a Japanese tank! It seemed out of place among the uneven terrain and the thick underbrush. But it was moving steadily toward them and it had the potential for much destruction.

Kowalsky dashed among his men. "We have got to knock that damned thing out. It has a lot of firepower. It could pour lots of fire into our lines. It could wipe us out."

He sent for more grenades. Tanks were powerful, but they were vulnerable. Since they moved on tracks that were attached to treads, Kowalsky planned to separate tracks and treads so that the tank would be immobile.

The monster was still over a hundred yards away. Enemy riflemen accompanied it for protection. Steadily and menacingly it crawled, its protectors ignorant of the fate awaiting them. Then Kowalsky gave the signal. Rifle and machine gun fire targeted those accompanying the tank. The grenades sought out the tracks of the tank.

The tank driver quickened the pace to escape the grenades. Suddenly, the tank whirled erratically and lurched out of control. Eventually it would face the direction from whence it came. Tracks and treads had now been separated. It was immobile. What next?

Patience was now needed. How many men were in the tank was not known. What everyone did know is that they eventually would have to come out. The simmering heat had pushed temperatures over the century mark. This could not be borne for long.

All eyes were now on the tank's turret. The attackers waited. After what seemed like hours, the turret was slowly lifted. The tank commander peered about cautiously, then retreated into the hold. The would-be protectors had been either killed or scattered. At some point, those within would have to come out.

Kowalsky's men now had the opening they sought. Situated on the high ground above the tank, they were ideally situated to launch more grenades. Two of the grenades plunged into the body of the tank. No one had anticipated the teeth-chattering noise that would ensue. The initial explosions almost lifted the tank into the air. The store of ammunition was being blown up. Machine gun shells scattered aimlessly, yet dangerously, in all directions. The din, once almost unbearable, soon became reduced to intermittent explosions. No Fourth of July parade in North Platte could have matched this. And no one in the tank could have survived.

"Nice work," Kowalsky kept repeating to his men. It wasn't much, but it was enough. They felt a real sense of accomplishment. On this day they had caused the enemy to flee and knocked out a potential source of destruction. Maybe there would be an end to the fighting that once seemed interminable.

Leonard and Rockwell planned future moves. Leonard understood the constant fire the troops had been under, but he saw the need to complete the task in order that it not be dragged out. "It's important that we keep going. Tomorrow will be the seventh day. With luck, we'll be at the foot of the hill."

Leonard also urged caution. "Remind the troops that anything is possible with the enemy. Assure them that we'll use our mortars should any attack occur. Our mortar guys have been doing a helluva job."

Leonard proved to be prophetic. The night would not be uneventful. The enemy did not disappoint. The all-too-familiar yelling and waving of arms accompanied the charge. The attackers were met with savage machine gun fire. Akers' squad, which seemed to be bearing the brunt of the attack, fortunately had acquired a number of Browning Automatic Rifles. The BAR's made a difference. The attack became a slaughter. Five or six enemy soldiers did reach the lines, only to be virtually obliterated by BAR bursts.

Then, as quickly as it started, it was over. Enemy casualties were immense. Some I Company losses were sustained. No matter what the disparity in numbers, it never was a good trade. The native stretcher-bearers continued their grim tasks.

Later communiqués would say that the "troops advanced doggedly" on the seventh day. Despite the damage that had been inflicted on them and the terrible losses in numbers, the enemy opposition seemed as resolute as ever. There would be no surrender. They would have to be killed.

Being assured the end was in sight sustained Rockwell's men. Flushing out of enemy positions went on. The Japanese soldiers often ran out of holes with guns firing, trying to inflict as much damage as they could before being gunned down. They never questioned why they had been placed in harm's way. It was an honor to die for the emperor.

The relative success of the day was occasionally interrupted when some of the company was pinned down. The enemy had them located, but their bullets could not reach them directly. Any attempt at moving forward or backward would be fatal. Leonard never hesitated in calling for mortar fire. These shells were delivered dangerously close to our own troops. Such close range was normally considered unthinkable. But this was no time for normalcy.

By late afternoon, it was apparent that I Company would take the territory that Captain Leonard had envisioned for that day. Now only the hill itself had to be taken. No matter that the troops did not yet know of the potential enormity of that task. That would be tomorrow. First there was the survival of the night.

Before daybreak squad leaders were passing on the stark details for the attack on the hill. Kowalsky's instructions were typical of what the remainder of the troops would hear.

"Today will be mean and nasty. We're going to be in the open at times without any cover. In some cases they may be firing point blank. If they pin you down, hug the ground as if you love it. Our mortar guys are the best. They have shells stacked next to their guns for as far as they can reach. We may have to pull back at times, but only temporarily. Forget about being scared. Remember what these guys did to Kramer."

The incremental ascent to the last two hundred yards of the hill was preceded by a mortar barrage that ordinary mortals seemingly could not endure. Both 60- and 81-millimeters were employed. The use of the artillery would have been too close and too dangerous.

Tragedy marred the beginning of the assault. The first outbreak of enemy machine gun fire claimed the life of Kowalsky, who was shot through the neck. He who had warned of today's dangers was a victim of them. "The Professor" had been held in awe by his men. The war had interrupted his college career. It seemed to his men that he should have been safely planning the war, not fighting it. But the times were desperate. The country was in jeopardy. Bodies were needed. No one was spared.

There was no time for grieving. Kennedy took over for Kowalsky even before the body bag arrived. The latter's family would receive the numbing news and it would be delivered by an impeccably attired and neatly scrubbed army officer. "We regret to inform you..." The telegrams all read the same. A gold star in the window would symbolize the family's loss. Kowalsky would fight no more, but he would be remembered, even extolled during patriotic celebrations. But Kowalsky's name would appear on no professor's class list. All too often, heroes die.

The men had yearned for open ground when they came to Leyte, but now was the wrong time for it. They were fully exposed and simply had to outthink, outshoot, and outluck their foes. The action began in earnest. About twenty enemy soldiers charged at Akers' squad. Because they were in the open, they became rifle and machine gun fodder. Three or four fought losing physical battles, but they did not perish without extracting their own damage. American survivors of this day would one day relive these events and deem what they did as impossible. And so most of it was.

Push forward and move back. Steady advance seemed impossible. Enemy charges could be seen as desperation, but they could cause unwanted damage.

The men slithered forward, not wanting to expose themselves by rising. The top of the Hill was in view. Later it would be learned that one of the company stormed enemy emplacements alone, inflicted much damage, and was slaughtered in the process. His family would be presented with the Medal of Honor, the nation's highest award for bravery. But American troops were never regarded as fanatics.

The top of the Hill lay immediately ahead. Now the time for advancing in slow stages was over. It was time for an assault of their own. Some of the enemy stood and fought. Some engaged in hand-to-hand fighting, alternately dying from rifle fire or crushed skulls. Some of the elite troops fled in panic. The vaunted Japanese First Division, having boasted that neither the Hill nor Leyte would be taken by their enemy, had been outfought and outlasted. In the end, it collapsed.

The next day I Company would learn that they and the 3rd Battalion had broken the "impregnable" Yamashita Line. Later they would learn that another American division had landed at Ormoc and began its push toward Limon and the Hill. By the end of the month they would know that Leyte was completely in American hands.

For the moment, the troops milled about in a daze. They had just endured eight days of unparalleled savagery. Each day seemed like the last. Kill or be killed; war offered no other option. The silence of the guns seemed eerie. One among them broke the silence by asking, "What day is it?"

Rockwell looked at his watch. It was December 7th.

Chapter 4

THE TRAIL

It had been named for a Spanish priest. It extended from Santa Maria to Santa Fe. The Villa Verde Trail was only eleven miles long as the crow flies. But men of the infantry don't fly. In reality, the trail zigged and zagged its way for over twenty-five miles. So much for crows.

Once again, Captain Leonard conferred with Rockwell: "I Company has its assignment here on Luzon. It's not a very glamorous one. We will not be making the attack on Manila. Our concentration will be on the Villa Verde Trail here in northern Luzon. The job is to clear the trail of the enemy and not allow them to help in the defense of Manila.

"The enemy has had plenty of time to prepare for our coming. They have the high ground. They are dug in. They are desperate. The commanding general of forces in the Philippines is commanding them. General Yamashita, that is. That's how serious they are about holding this trail."

"What happens if we capture him?" asked Rockwell, half kiddingly.

Leonard answered seriously. "The unit that captures him will probably be relieved and sent somewhere for rest and relaxation."

Then Leonard detailed the role of I Company in the clearing of the trail. "It's only ten to twelve feet wide in some places. It's best suited for water buffalo dragging carts. The terrain is unfriendly. There are hills upon hills. There are sharp ridges and deep ravines. It's a challenge."

Despite having recited obstacles that would have overwhelmed lesser mortals, Leonard talked only of success. He was a warrior that inspired others to be so. The trail would be cleared of the enemy. It was only a matter of time.

Rockwell summoned his squad leaders in order to relay the battle plans. "If some of your men seem overwhelmed, remind them of what they have achieved. They said we couldn't take Hill 400, and we did. They said we couldn't take Leyte, and we did. Sure, this looks tougher. There are lots of hills. The enemy must have elaborate pill boxes. We'll have to go cave by cave. Then there is thick underbrush and even kunai grass that helps to shield their positions. What the hell, we'll do it. It'll just take a little more time."

"How long does he think this will take?" asked Akers.

"It looks like months, not days. The captain talks in terms of three months."

"How about manpower?" asked Pickens. "Our ranks are pretty thin. I don't have a full squad. We have been promised troops before. Where the hell are they?"

Rockwell responded quickly to avert any malaise. "You know the captain will deliver. He always does. He fights for his men. If the captain promises, bet on it."

Kennedy wondered about estimates of the strength of the enemy. "What kind of weapons do they have?"

"Apparently they have more artillery than before. And they have some tanks. Otherwise, it is rifles and machine guns and mortars. The worst part is that they are dug in and have had lots of time to prepare. We've got to find them and rout them out. It'll take a while."

Akers thought of how he would broach the topic to his squad. "I guess we can keep spirits up by reminding the men of what they've done. They've done everything the enemy said couldn't be done. Now the enemy vows that the trail can't be taken. It's impossible. But those who win are those who do the impossible."

Pickens wondered what kept their foes going, "The emperor must be a wonderful guy."

The Igorots arrived. These mountain men of Luzon were a welcome sight. Their arrival meant that food, supplies, and ammunition had been delivered. Who else could have transported goods over and up such unfriendly terrain?

But the presence of the Igorots was also ominous. Now that they had unloaded their goods, everyone knew what they would carry on their return trip. It would be the bodies of the lifeless and those clinging to life. They would negotiate the steep slopes as if they were level ground. They saved countless lives by so doing. But who would be the victims in the days ahead?

The men in Kennedy's squad talked as they prepared for the days ahead.

"This seems like the same damned thing over and over. We get our orders. We fight. We lose a lot of good men. We kill every one of those bastards. It's over. Then we start all over."

"Maybe there's another way of looking at it. Back in New Guinea, we were the ones being attacked at the beginning. It took a while for us to get on the offensive. Hell, at least we're closer to the end."

"Yeah, but how long is it going to take? Some of the guys have been over here three years. The longer they stay, the greater their chances of being hit or killed. How many years is it going to take?"

"I've heard people say as much as ten years. We can already see how desperate they are. They know that some of their guys have been smothered in caves. Think of how gruesome the sight is of some of them on fire because of the flamethrowers. But still they fight, and more vicious than ever."

"Maybe we'll get some help. Replacements are on the way. The war in Europe will end before this one. Things will get better."

Kennedy had heard some of the speculation. "All that talk about the future is well and good, but we push off tomorrow. We go day to day. Let others plan the future. We have to worry about today and then tomorrow. Otherwise, the war will be over for us any moment."

At dawn of the next day, the inevitable barrage jolted the hills and echoed down the deep ravines. It exhumed some trees and leveled kunai grass. For all its intended ferocity, however, the shells would cause little loss of life, so well entrenched in their deep and elaborate caves were the enemy. Most of them not only endured, but seemed to fight more determinedly.

As I Company pushed off to eventually rid the trail of the enemy, they became fully aware that the shelling had not obliterated the men of Nippon. Enemy machine gun fire erupted immediately. This had been anticipated, and a process for eliminating machine gun nests was to be used many times over.

After softening up the machine gun nests with mortar and machine gun fire, men crawled near the entrance to the cave and fired random shots to keep the enemy from the entrance. Now a lethal homemade creation was put into play. It consisted of blocks of TNT that were wired to a board from a ration box, and all this tied to a bamboo pole. All that was left was to light the fuse and throw the Bamboo Bomb into the cave.

Most, but not all of the deafening noise was squelched by the cave. Rocks still flew, smoke belched, and leaves flew. There would be no signs of life. There was no concern about any brutality inflicted on the cave dwellers. The machine gun would chatter no more.

There was no respite from the dangers of the war. As Akers' squad rounded a corner, a single shot rang out. Callahan lay dead. Then another shot. Abruzzi became the second fatality.

"Sniper!" yelled Akers. "Get back. Get back. Don't let the bastard kill any more of us. Let me get Rockwell on the radio."

Rockwell ordered a halt while plans were made to locate and exterminate the sniper. Frustration set in. The sniper was holding up an entire battalion. How many more would have been killed if the contingent tried to move ahead?

"Let's put the M4 tank we have to work," said Rockwell. "See if we can get the bastard to fire on it. Maybe we can level some trees and hope he's in one of them. Let's see what machinery can do."

The tank hovered into view. It moved slowly along the narrow and hazardous trail. Brush was leveled as the behemoth advanced. Finally, it reached the corner.

Meanwhile, men from Pickens' squad were deployed on the bank above the trail. They were to look for the whereabouts of the sniper. Company mortars were poised to help end the stalemate. The tank's machine guns were manned.

"All of this for one goddamned sniper," muttered Pickens. "He's holding up the whole operation."

The tank turned the corner. The sniper fired as if to taunt the tank. Surely, he was no match, but he was in control as long as his location was unknown to the attackers. The tank men sprayed and even leveled some trees. For the moment, at least, the sniper was silent. The standoff lingered to dusk. I Company would dig in and wait for another day.

Meanwhile, the promised replacements arrived. Captain Leonard had delivered again. Although they were a motley lot, they were a welcome sight. Each would have a different story to tell for how the luck of the draw had placed them in this place at this time. Some had some infantry training, but most did not. They would learn by doing. Welcome to the club.

Squad leaders offered an orientation as best they could. The newly arrived had been thrust into a situation that they had neither anticipated nor requested. Some were stunned, others were troubled, and all had reasons to be scared.

Pickens' greeting to them would be typical. "You stay alive around here by being smart and learning fast. Your rifle and your helmet are your best friends. Never be without them. Never. Some of your new buddies will try to scare the hell out of you and others will tell you not to worry. They're both wrong. There's plenty to worry about and you'll be scared soon enough. Now let me tell you what we're up to."

Most of what they were told was too much, too fast. It all happened so swiftly. For days en route they had speculated as to what their fate might be. They had kidded about the luck of the draw. So far, this assignment looked like bad luck.

So much for instructions. The clearing of the trail must go on. Newly refurbished with replacements, the first elements of I Company approached the corner. Yesterday the results there had been deadly. Had the sniper survived? Could the company afford to be held up further? How many more lives were they willing to concede?

They slinked around the corner one by one. The silence seemed ominous. Was the sniper waiting to pick his spots? The rest of the company passed the corner cautiously and uneventfully. No sniper was heard from. For the moment, at least, he was history.

Another machine gun nest was heard from. It had to be erased. Mortar shells rained in on it. Rifle shots were fired to keep the occupants inside. And now the infamous Bamboo, fully lit, came into play. The results were truly deadly.

The replacements looked on in awe and amazement. So this was what war was all about? It was not like the movies. No one looked or acted like John Wayne. He remained in Hollywood. No wonder he always survived.

Now one of the replacements was the first to spot a couple of tanks, located on the rim of a deep ravine. They appeared to be abandoned, since the kunai grass had grown tall enough to all but cover them. Curiosity and inexperience on the part of replacements Corr and Gordon drew them toward the tanks for closer examination. The caution that Sergeant Kennedy urged upon them was forgotten, if indeed it was ever remembered. Both walked toward the tanks as carefree as if this were a picnic.

What followed was no picnic. Too late they recognized bunkers carved into the embankment aside the tanks. Out from the nearby holes emerged several enemy riflemen. Corr and Gordon were rendered 24-hour heroes. Those at home would never hear mention either of their foolishness or of the horror of their deaths.

This was particularly true in Gordon's case. His death was gruesome. A hail of fire separated his head from his body. The head spun crazily on the ground, taking forever to stop.

However intended, the folly of the recruits did unearth a potentially dangerous situation. What if the company had merely passed on? What if the company were cut in half?

But this was no time for questions. The enemy soldiers, about twenty in number, were in full view. The firefight that ensued might have set records for the ammunition expended. Overkill might describe it best. Rifle fire, bazookas, BAR's, and grenades contributed to the carnage. Finally, there was an attackers' charge at the holes where the enemy first appeared. Bazookas did the rest. Enemy dead studded the tank area. I Company lost Justice and Scalapino, two veterans from New Guinea. Seven of their comrades were readied for the aid station. The Igorots had their return cargo.

The day had been grueling. Obliterating machine gun nests and neutralizing caves had become such a matter of course that no count of them was known or kept. The fire fight was a horror show that left the men spent emotionally and exhausted physically. And there was always those endless number of hills.

Bailey of Akers' squad said it best. "The hills are bad enough, but the worst part is what's in those hills. We have to fight our way up and over. Is there no end to these bastards?"

As they dug in for the night, all of them looked forward to the rest they deserved. Alas, both nature and man would conspire to render those yearnings mere pipe dreams.

First, the deluge. The rains that had been forecast for this time of year arrived as if on cue. These were not harmless showers. Monsoon would be a more appropriate description. The downpours caused havoc in terms of comfort and safety. Foxholes became virtual swimming pools in some instances, making any decent sleep a casualty. The threat of mudslides was real. Washouts along the trail could prevent the passage of troops. The army engineers, equipped with armored vehicles, would have to make the trail more negotiable. For the moment, the rain cascaded down the ravines, carved ruts in the trail, and soaked all living things. And it seemed without end.

"As if we didn't have enough to worry about. What else can happen to us?" asked Balzano, one of the replacements.

He would not relish the answer. Suddenly, there was a terrifying commotion. The yelling was loud, constant, and endless. The enemy was among them. The men in the company acted on instinct. It was kill or be killed. Shoot, club, smash. Survival was in the hands of fate. Akers shot three who had charged the lines unarmed, merely as cannon fodder. Pickens was grazed by a bayonet before he could recover and riddle his foe with bullets. Connors conducted a virtual shooting gallery before being hit from behind, never to recover. The infiltrators preferred to fight at night, but none would recover from this night. Sixty-three dead sons of Nippon would be counted in the morning. Five I Company men had fought their last battle and four more required aid station attention.

Akers was too exhausted to damn what had happened. He merely spit in disgust.

In the morning downpour, the company surveyed the damage inflicted by nature and man. The heavy rains produced rivulets, ruts, and washouts along the trail. The enemy bodies, some piled like mounds of dirt and others lying in bunches, were virtually ignored. On another day, they would have to be reckoned with; the stench would become almost unbearable.

Enter the engineers. They now occupied center stage. Usually dispatched to create and repair airstrips away from the battle, they now became point men in it. Their bulldozers were armored and machine gun equipped. They added to the company firepower.

Welcome as the presence and the work of the engineers was, their mere existence caused problems for the company. Chief among them was that the commotion caused by the machinery gave away any secrecy the company may have had. In addition, it galvanized the enemy, who could not be expected to remain bystanders when the trail was being reconstructed so that the foot soldiers could advance upon them.

Japanese reaction was almost immediate. They emerged from their hideouts and pushed their highly maneuverable 75-millimeter gun into position. Firing upon the bulldozer began. The dozer sought refuge in the density of the trees. The company artillery would do the retaliating. Eighty-one mortar shells also whistled in. Enemy survivors abandoned the gun. Eventually it would end its tour of duty in the deep ravine below.

For now, the advance was stalled by a host of factors. Supplies of food and ammunition were desperately needed. The rugged terrain and frequent deluges made the delivery of provisions and supplies a nightmare. By now their very lack brought the company to a standstill. While the troops were concerned with matters of life and death, days had become weeks and then weeks a month or more. Now they could only wait for the arrival of the Igorots.

The wait afforded time for reflection among the veterans and newcomers alike. Fordha, the crusty machine gunner who joined the outfit in the last days of the New Guinea campaign, set the stage. "The only good thing about this dump is the smell of the pine trees. It reminds me of being home in Wisconsin. I wish I were."

"Well, you gotta figure that life in Wisconsin would be hell if these bastards were in charge," countered Yates. "And how the hell can you smell those trees now? I smell those rotten, stinking bodies."

Those new to the company were no longer rookies. Thrown into action, they became veterans in one day. Kroll from Philadelphia told of his experience. "This whole thing is crazy. I trained in the field artillery. I never fired this rifle. I was assigned to Fort Bragg as an instructor. We were training troops for Europe. Suddenly, I got orders for San Francisco. And here I am. If I survive this war, I should write a book. But no one would believe it."

Pelosi from Connecticut agreed. "Nothing in our training prepared us for this. There's something different every day. You learn or you die. And even that may not be enough. We've lost some very good men just because their number seemed to be up."

Sanford, a veteran of the outfit from its days in the States, joined in. "In the long run, experience is the best teacher. Those of us who captured the Hill in Leyte were better prepared for this. We've been through banzai attacks and all kinds of whacky stuff. I don't know how you guys would have stood up under it."

The company dug in, not knowing how long the wait for supplies would entail. The food supply, which consisted mainly of the much-maligned K rations, was in danger of depletion. "I never thought I would be eagerly awaiting the arrival of K rations," laughed McLaughlin.

The shortage of food turned out to be not the only problem. The enemy saw to that. On the second night of the wait, at least ten of them charged the perimeter in the area of Kennedy's squad. Minor in number in comparison, the enemy attackers made up for it in fury and effect. Pierce, Dennison, and Lewinsky were killed immediately and Berra and Costopolous would be taken to the aid station. The firefight had been brief, but furious, and with no breakthroughs. Ten enemy corpses would litter the soggy terrain when it was over. I Company could not afford such steady losses. The company was reverting to its numbers before the most recent addition of replacements.

On the fourth day of waiting, the Igorots arrived. The little men of Luzon were dwarfed by the loads they bore. They had negotiated the hills, overcome the effects of the monsoon-like rain, and handled the deep ravines. They brought something for everyone: food, ammunition, supplies, even mail. Still smiling despite the exhaustion they must have felt, the native men were genuinely admired by the troops.

"These guys should get medals."

"They have no fear."

"They know that if they're captured by the Japs, they'll be tortured to death."

Captain Leonard, though fiercely impatient with the waiting, moved among the troops to buoy their spirits. "Good work. We've got them on the run," he repeated over and over.

More additions to the company meant more admiration for their captain. He was no stranger to the front lines. He himself had killed significant numbers of the enemy. He had been wounded three times, but always returned with new resolve. For the comparative newcomers, watching him up close only verified the lore that they had heard heretofore.

"The man would never send us where he would not go," said Kingsley. That seemed to say it for all.

The captain now met with Rockwell and the squad leaders. "We've got to expect that the enemy is going to be more fanatic than ever, if that's possible. We know they are toughest when their situation turns hopeless. It's as if they know they are losing the war, but they won't admit defeat."

Leonard anticipated questions about the availability of replacements. He knew that the numbers in the ranks were not at the level of the last addition. "Help is on the way. I have been promised more troops and they will be here any day now. Get them oriented as quickly as possible. We want them to live."

Meanwhile, the advance would continue in the morning. The men of the company knew that the enemy would not have been idle during the days of waiting. They should expect resistance every step of the way.

The Japanese did not disappoint, but the carnage was lethal to them. Cave after cave was blown up or burned out. The fighting over the next four days would cost them 220 men. A total of forty caves would be destroyed. The company arsenal had been expanded to include more lethal weapons, such as more bazookas and flamethrowers. So bitter was the fighting that the horrific sight of enemy soldiers lit afire brought no gasps from men of the company. The action in Manila might be commanding the headlines, but the most ruthless phase of the war was being played out here on the Villa Verde.

Leonard ordered a stay in the advance, if only to regroup. More replacements arrived, as the captain had promised. The company numbers had dwindled to scandalous proportions, having reached about half strength. Although the company losses paled in comparison with enemy numbers, the cost of four days of fighting was 21 dead and 23 wounded. Even at that rate, the price was too much.

Again, the replacements were a varied lot, and tales of how they found themselves in these circumstances left both the narrators and listeners bewildered. Many had no infantry training. Some had been in positions where they were destined never to see front line action. Now they were in a situation whose seriousness could not be overemphasized. If they were lucky overnight, the war would not begin for them until the next day.

That day began as the previous day had ended: more nests and caves, more destruction, more men on fire. There seemed to be no respite. The enemy contested every inch. Around the noon hour, a band of about twenty men charged from the cover of the thick underbrush and the kunai grass. Their very numbers signaled that they were intent on inflicting as much damage as possible, no matter what the price.

The firefight that ensued set records for ammunition use. The fighting was so close that only rifles and machine guns could be used. Finally, the enemy was out in the open. It was kill or be killed. It was all over in minutes, with over twenty enemy dead lying in piles. Four company men were dead, two among them yesterday's replacements. Fate was unkind.

Weeks became a month. The struggle on the trail was nearing the end of its third month. Enemy attacks became less frequent, but more ferocious. The way to Santa Fe would not be easy.

"Don't these little bastards ever quit?" asked Krauss, one of the new replacements.

"They don't ever think about it," responded Kennedy. "They're dying for the emperor."

"They can't let us take this trail. Their commanding general in the Pacific is leading them. He has vowed never to surrender," said Caruso, a wily veteran of Leyte and New Guinea. "They keep saying we can't break some goddamned line of theirs. We've crossed so many of their lines that I can't remember the name of the one now. Who cares what the hell they call it? We'll cross that one, too."

Now Captain Leonard met with Rockwell. It was obvious that he had more than the matter of moral support on his mind. "General Hill is pleased with our advance, but he believes the enemy is bleeding us to death. Why we don't have lots of replacements available now that the war is over in Europe frustrates the hell out of all of us. Anyway, Hill wants to try something different. He's calling for a cease fire tomorrow. We will not attack. Our observation planes will drop leaflets to the Japanese, asking them to surrender. An enemy prisoner has written the script for the leaflet, which asks his comrades to surrender because all is lost. The Japs are asked to attach the leaflet to a stick and wave it as they head for our lines. Their safety is guaranteed. I can't emphasize enough that there must be no shooting. None. That's what the hell a cease fire is all about."

Rockwell seemed unconvinced. "Do you really think this will work? You mean to say that those bastards will give themselves up? Is the general serious?"

It was unusually brazen for Rockwell to ever question his captain's orders and he seemed mildly shocked that he had done so. Captain Leonard was in no mood to debate. He had his orders. "Look, who would have thought a week ago that there would be any prisoners? Now, one of their own writes this leaflet. I have my orders. Now you have yours. Be damned sure your men have their orders for tomorrow." He strode off with the last word.

The new day dawned. Would this be the day when the battle for the trail would end? Would this be merely a one-day interruption in the war? While the shooting was supposed to stop, the men had to be prepared for the possible arrival of prisoners. Rockwell had brooked no nonsense in relaying Leonard's message to his squad leaders.

"Make no bones about it to your men. There is to be absolutely no shooting. Any dumb sonofabitch who forgets that will have a long time to remember. You've seen the leaflets. Some were dropped into our lines. Search any prisoner for weapons. Be prepared for trickery. I'll turn them over to G-2, the intelligence guys. I don't know if this scheme will work or not, but it's not our business to question orders. We're soldiers. It's our job to obey."

The day was unusual. The enemy soldiers, usually masters of concealment, now exposed themselves for all to see on a not-too-distant ridge. They sauntered back and forth, as if to test the sincerity of their foes. Were they merely taunting? Were they just welcoming a day off from the war? Or were they merely delaying coming to the American lines?

By the noon hour there were no surrenders. "I don't detect any mass defections," said a cynical Kelly.

"They're probably waiting for the last minute," said a more hopeful Guerritz.

"Maybe other companies have had better luck," said Rockwell.

"How could anyone turn down a chance to get through the war alive?" wondered a newly arrived Soloway.

As dusk neared, realism replaced idealism. Maybe became never. They should have known that this had been merely a pipe dream. Worse still, the enemy might cap the day with a night attack. It would be "just like those bastards." What the hell was the general thinking when he decided on such a day? Maybe he should visit the front lines more often. You learn things there.

No night attack did take place, but the morning was another story. Enemy artillery, inactive of late, shattered the peace by laying in rounds of shells. "Those bastards," yelled Akers, "did they use yesterday to plan this?" Then, like others, he scrambled for cover.

The company observers reported more trouble. Enemy tanks were on the way. It had seemed a forgone conclusion that the trail in that vicinity was too narrow for tanks. Once again, the enemy seemed to be defying all reason. Here came the tanks, however slowly.

Now Captain Leonard swung into action. Artillery and mortar batteries had to be called upon. Pickens opted to act as a forward observer to direct the shelling, but McBride begged his squad leader for the role. The latter climbed the hill and moved into position to advise company guns.

What followed was a mortar and artillery duel. Much was at stake. The Americans were dangerously close to clearing the trail. The enemy seemed intent not only of stemming the company's advance, but also in breaking through the lines to cause chaos and retreat. Wasn't it nice that they had a day to plan this?

Men of the company dug furiously and deep. Shrapnel from the shells would have been deadly for anyone remaining at ground level. But enemy shelling became sporadic, then non-existent. McBride must have done a helluva observation job.

As Pickens rushed to direct his squad, he caught sight of stretcher bearers who were carrying a body down the hill. Pickens couldn't resist a look. It was McBride! He was very much alive, but Pickens sickened when McBride peeled off the blanket to reveal that he had lost much of his right leg.

The squad leader had no time to express his sorrow. McBride spared him that anyway. Knowing Pickens' remorse and the twists of fate, McBride gave him a "thumbs up" sign. Sure, this could have happened to Pickens, but there was never any satisfactory explanation of who got hurt and who escaped unscathed. The war was over for McBride, but tales of his courage and spirit would become a prominent part of company lore.

There was still the matter of the enemy tanks. Pickens' squad had crawled their way to a point overlooking the trail. Equipped with an extra supply of grenades, their task was to immobilize the lead tank. As they had done on Leyte, they must separate the tank's treads from its tracks.

Pickens was explicit. "Make every grenade count. Aim for the tracks. We can't let these bastards get through or they'll shoot the hell out of us. If we stop the lead tank, the others can't get by. They'll have to retreat and they'll have a helluva time turning around. This trail isn't exactly Route 66."

Only minutes later, the first tank rounded the corner. Men appeared on either side for protection. The tank proceeded, oblivious to the fate intended for it. Its goal was to pierce the adversary's lines and force a retreat. Yesterday they were supposed to have surrendered. Today they were on the attack. The Americans were advancing closer to the end of the trail. They must be stopped.

At this point, Pickens and his squad were perched directly above the lead tank. Its protectors crouched and looked ahead intently. They were poised to eliminate any dangers to their crawling monster. But they had no notion of what lay above them.

Pickens had rehearsed the next step with his men. The "surprise party" he had named it. His men awaited the signal. "Now," he whispered. The grenades rained down. All hell ensued. Three enemy soldiers lay on the trail immobile, presumably dead. The lead tank stopped. Was it immobilized?

Rockwell radioed Leonard immediately. "The tanks are stopped. It looks as if it would be a picnic for the artillery guys."

Down on the trail the enemy was in disarray. They had proceeded so effortlessly, so confidently to this point. Nothing appeared to be in their way. Their plan of attack was to have foot soldiers follow a successful tank breakthrough. They would take the trail back into their own hands. But now, this horrible setback.

The lead tank had been rendered immobile. Those that followed were trapped. Despite all their firepower, they could not get into position to fire their artillery and their machine guns. Now useless, the behemoths sought to retreat. It was an exercise in maneuverability. Forward and backward they moved within the narrowness of the trail. Moving too close to the edge of the trail might lead to a plunge to certain death in the ravine below. The task seemed endless, and it was. Yesterday's planned breakthrough now became today's nightmare.

Leonard called for the artillery to destroy the tanks. To prepare for the attack, he ordered a company pullback to avoid any errant friendly fire. Once zeroed in, the artillery began its destruction. The would-be protectors of the tanks disintegrated, some safely and others not so fortunate. The tank attack was history, but so were any thoughts of enemy surrender.

The battle for the Villa Verde Trail entered its fourth month. It seemed secondary to the fight for Manila, but not so in intensity. Every gain was at a price. Enemy assaults often defied reason and they haunted the men of I Company. Although the number of American casualties seemed puny aside enemy losses, the attackers lamented that replacements seemed as necessary as supplies. And, having been promised that the end was near, the men grew impatient.

"I wish we could get this damned thing over with," said Miles.

"I hope I never see another trail," muttered Rogers.

"Maybe we should all be happy if we get out of here alive," cautioned Akers.

The war resumed in earnest. Hill 23 was the target of the day. It was the highest point on the trail. From there, it was a stone's throw through the Carabello Mountains and down to the Cagayan Valley.

Uphill. It was always uphill. More bunkers and more machine gun nests. All the various weapons of death would be used by the attackers. More bazookas were available. Makeshift bamboo bombs and even a flamethrower were ready. Damn the bastards who had taken advantage of the cease fire. They would get what they had earned.

The "softening up" by the artillery began. The blasts leveled trees and flattened kunai grass. The approach up the hill was cluttered and cleared at the same time.

And out they moved once again. The way was barely negotiable. The troops passed warily among the abandoned tanks and dead bodies. The order had been passed to "touch nothing," lest booby traps awaited the curious. The tanks had so scarred the trail that the engineers would go to work as soon as that part of the trail was secured.

No amount of artillery shelling seemed able to silence enemy machine guns. No advance was possible until the position of the machine gunners was located and obliterated. It was all so brutal, but the inhumanity was not an issue. The goal was to take the hill. The end justified the means.

The company movement up the hill seemed ponderously slow. To call it an advance might be an overstatement. Now the mortar guys, fully experienced with providing support, seemed to outdo themselves. In some cases they scored direct hits at the door of the bunkers. This hastened the advance. Bazooka blasts silenced some emplacements. The dreaded flamethrowers caused some of the enemy to run from their hideouts fully aflame. Usually, gunners spared them continuing horror. Pretty it was not.

As the company pressed on, squad leaders alerted the men for the possibility of an enemy attack. All signs pointed to one. The situation was becoming more desperate for the enemy. The advantage of the high ground was slipping away. The end was in sight. There was no mystery as to what fate awaited those who held out. But the attack never came.

Squad leaders took inventory of their numbers. As usual, the advance was exacted at a cost. Four were dead, and nine more wounded. The latter were headed to the aid station. Akers, the grisly veteran, shook his head. "Whoever said that war doesn't settle who's right, but who's left, had it about right."

What followed was beyond the wildest imagination of the troops. There would be no fight for the crest of the hill! After four months of the most savage fighting in the Philippines, the finish was to have no flourish. The enemy had uncharacteristically withdrawn, apparently to live and fight and kill another day. After four months, it would end like this?

Now I Company had the high ground. After climbing and fighting up so many hills, they had taken their last one. Most of the troops tried to enjoy the moment, leaving to their superiors the task of what it all meant.

Warren slumped to the ground in exhaustion. "Did we just cross another line we weren't supposed to?"

"Yeah," said Cunningham, in a manner that indicated he was keeping score. "It was another Yamashita line."

"Who the hell is Yamashita?"

Again, Cunningham was a storehouse of information. "He's the commander of all the Jap forces in the Philippines. He's been in charge here on the trail. That's how important this fight is."

Simpson wondered about the whereabouts of Yamashita. "Is he still here?"

"He's still up here somewhere. Wouldn't it be great if we captured him?"

Most of the men dismissed the idea of capturing Yamashita alive as a pipe dream. Agganis spoke for many of them. "Do you think he'd let himself be captured? He'd kill himself first. 'Dying for the emperor' they'll call it."

Hill switched from one form of speculation to another. "At least we can rest for awhile. It doesn't make sense they would give up this hill without a fight and then attack us from below."

Alas, Hill had spoken just as Rockwell happened by. "Damn it, soldier, these bastards never make sense. The whole goddamned war doesn't make sense. Forget about what makes sense. What makes sense is for all of you to get off your butts and get a perimeter set up. They know we're here. Dig deep or you might not dig another hole. Now let's get at it."

No more urging was required. The digging went on in earnest. The perimeter was established but doubts existed among the men about any impending attack.

"If Yamashita is such a great general, why would he let us take this hill without a fight?" asked Pickens, after making sure that Rockwell was not within earshot.

Sims was beyond any speculation. "Look, we've dug our foxhole. This war is about one damned foxhole after another. What's wrong with being extra careful?"

"Yeah, but when I get home I'm going to give away every shovel that I might own," said Antonelli. "I've dug too many holes. They'll be no more digging for me."

Darkness enveloped the hill. Guards were on duty at each foxhole. The long night started eerily quiet, interrupted only by the unnerving sounds of playful monkeys.

And then the warned-about attack started to become a harsh reality. Flares lit the hill as if it were high noon. The whistle and explosion of mortar shells followed. Machine guns chattered. And then they charged uphill, not singly, but in droves. I Company might have been given the hill, but now they had to fight like hell to keep it.

All the warnings and the preparations had not been idle exercises. Any doubts about their wisdom vanished with the landing of the first mortar shell. The attack seemed to be coming from three sides. Company machine guns sprayed the hillside as the screaming attackers sought to advance. Grenades were both thrown and rolled down the hill, resulting in terrible carnage. Occasionally, an attacker would reach the crest, but only long enough to be riddled with bullets.

The attack seemed to have no other rationale than that the enemy soldiers would be too numerous to wipe out. The defenders indeed worried about their guns becoming too hot to fire. Strangely, the attackers continued to charge directly into American guns. It contributed to their undoing.

Then, as suddenly as the attack had begun, it was over. The last gasp of retaining the Villa Verde Trail by the enemy was over. The price was enormous. The dead body count would later reveal to be 109. I Company losses were three dead and seven wounded.

By midday the company moved to clear the remainder of the trail. There proved to be no opposition. The major discovery was of six abandoned huts, built by the Igorots and now abandoned by the Japanese. To some it seemed like a very small prize for four months of misery.

The realization of what had been accomplished would come later. The Villa Verde Trail had been cleared from the central plains of Luzon through the Carabello Mountains. The lush Cagayan Valley lay below. Another "impregnable" line had been crossed. And just in time.

Downpours, fog, washouts, and landslides followed. But they did not fire back.

Commendations from the commanding general were congratulatory, but foreboding.

"I look for your continued success in the heart of Tokyo," it read in part. There was always more.

Chapter 5

THE MOP-UP

August 15 was to be the most momentous day of the war, yet I Company would fire no shots. Its events were unanticipated, and thus impossible to fully comprehend. It seemed to call for wild celebration, yet it was greeted with an inexplicable numbness.

A month had passed since the clearing of the trail. It had been a confusing period. Contact with the enemy occurred through aggressive patrolling. Rumors abounded that some of the longest serving veterans would be sent home. Movies became a nightly fare. Given the daily fights for survival that the company had experienced, it all seemed surreal.

On the other hand, there were constant reminders that the war was still going on and people were being killed. Forty-four of the enemy were killed and twenty-two had been captured in one day. What the enemy lacked in organization, they compensated for with fanaticism.

At other times, the company prepped for the future. It was known to all the men that Operation Olympic, the invasion of Japan, had a D Day of November 1, 1945. Over and over the men could recite the details. The island of Kyushu. The city of Sasebo. I Company in the second of three waves. Japan arming every man, woman, and child to prevent any invasion. It was all so big that it was beyond all understanding. Why worry?

So it was on this significant day that Pickens and his squad, armed with their mess kits, began their climb up the hill to the mess tent. Suddenly, gunfire interrupted the morning calm. Instinctively, the men dove for cover. Just as quickly, Pickens realized that it was not enemy fire. Rather, it was coming from advancing Filipino soldiers, who were firing shots aimlessly into the air.

After reciting a litany of expletives that insured Pickens his good standing within the non-commissioned ranks, Pickens accosted the men. "What the hell are you doing? Stop wasting ammunition!"

The Filipino soldiers were visibly shaken. Where normally their use of the English language could have served as a model for most I Company men to adopt, now they were overwhelmed. One blurted, "Big bomb, big bomb. War's over."

Pickens would have none of it. "Yeah, the war's over. It's all over these goddamned mountains. Now get the hell out of here and save your ammo for the Japs."

Pickens and his men were prepared to talk no more of what was said by the Filipinos. They regarded their allies as easily excitable, and just as easily duped. The war's end seemed so distant that any speculation about its ending was an idle exercise at best. At its worst, it could serve as a cruel hoax.

As the men entered the mess tent, they noted a buzz in the atmosphere that was unusual. Normally, breakfast was a relatively quiet meal, if only because the troops had been awakened from a sound slumber. This morning was different. It was all about the news being spread by the Filipino soldiers.

Comparatively little food was consumed, the men's appetite being whetted more by the dramatic reports. Many still could not believe it, fearing the mental depression that would accompany any false hopes.

"How do we know it's true?" asked Conyers.

It was a question that everyone wanted answered. Did it come from the Filipinos alone? Did anyone see it in writing? What did Captain Leonard have to say?

"It was in *Stars and Stripes*," answered Salvetti. "Lots of guys say they saw it there."

The cynics still prevailed. Markey typified them. "Where in *Stars and Stripes*? How come there's not a single copy here? If this is a joke, someone is going to pay dearly."

By the time the men returned to the company perimeter, Captain Leonard had delivered the official news. Now it could be believed. There indeed had been a "Big Bomb." In fact there were two. They had caused so much killing and destruction that the Emperor did what had been considered unthinkable. He had called for surrender to spare his people further carnage. Given the negligible number of the enemy that had capitulated in New Guinea or the Philippines, few could fathom the report at first.

Surprisingly, even when the report the men almost feared to believe was fully substantiated, there were few of the loud outbursts of joy that were to be expected. First there was relief. They had survived. No more war. Now thoughts could turn to family or girlfriends. If only it could be true!

It was unbelievable. Or was it?

Yes, it was officially alright to believe the reports. But, as usual, the army was expert in dampening spirits. Yes, the war was over, but there were still over 1,500 to 1,800 of the enemy in the battalion area. Some of these did not know the war was over. Many of the others refused to accept it. Peace was official, if not actual, in northern Luzon. It did not leave I Company in a celebratory mood.

Akers gave the official word to his squad. "We have our orders. There is to be no fighting after this day, August 15. Understand? Thousands of leaflets are being dropped into Japanese lines. The leaflets tell them that the emperor orders them to surrender. Remember, as much as we may hate them, they should be allowed to surrender peacefully. The war is over."

All of this left the men in a state of frustration and exasperation. After 654 days of combat, peace wasn't supposed to be like this. You were supposed to go home and be grateful you survived. It meant reunions and parties. It meant reuniting with a girlfriend or being in demand by new ones. It meant no more war. But now you weren't sure what to expect.

"Some peace we've got," began Walker. "How can you stop fighting when they don't want to?"

"This is scary," said Edwards. "We're still not safe. I remember reading that soldiers were killed after World War I."

"Suppose they don't surrender. We'll have to go out on patrols to find them and bring them in," said Rosenberg. "Who the hell is going to volunteer for this?"

"I have no hopes that they will surrender," said Noel. "Remember the day we had on the trail? Did they surrender then?"

Further word from Captain Leonard assured the men that they had no monopoly on concern. He ordered foxholes to be dug, guard duty to be vigilant, and a wartime posture to be maintained until the enemy had proved its willingness to surrender.

The skeptics were right. There was no surrendering. Worse still, reality returned two nights later in the form of a full-throated banzai charge. No break in the lines occurred, but the attack was not without its cost. Hill was killed, and Rockford and Zarchen were hit. The morning count of enemy dead was forty-nine. There were no prisoners.

Now the life and death choices that the company leaders had had to make throughout the war became more difficult than ever. Selecting men for patrols placed them in harm's way. Just days ago the war seemed to be over and men had expressed gratitude for surviving it. How silly all that seemed now.

Judging the success or failure of a patrol seemed to defy reason in the eyes of the men. When no enemy was found and all members returned safely, they considered the patrol a success. On the other hand, if an enemy concentration was discovered and even if there were company casualties, the leaders considered that a success. None of the men could be convinced.

Pickens was chosen to conduct the first patrol. He never flinched, selecting a mixture of veterans and relative newcomers. Away from the lines, Pickens told his stories and showed his love for a good time. But he didn't look upon patrols with amusement. Now was the time to put the war face on, bring in the enemy, and do it without loss or injury to I Company personnel.

The patrol was briefed on its mission. Its destination was the village of Tacoban, two miles to the northwest. A pocket of the enemy was reportedly located there. Some, but not all, were expected to be armed. The goal was to bring them in, while guaranteeing their safety. But when in doubt, shoot.

The patrol proceeded cautiously. No reminders of the need for vigilance was needed. Tacoban was reached on cue.

Pickens sought out the mayor of the village, who appeared with a small entourage.

"Are there Japs in these hills?" asked the squad leader.

"Oh yes," replied the mayor. "Lots of them."

"Do you know where they are?"

The mayor pointed. "I think they're somewhere up that trail."

Now Pickens tried to bring the mission closer to home. "Do you have anyone who would be a guide for us?"

The mayor turned for a discussion with his party. The talk was animated. Filipino troops had fought loyally alongside their American counterparts throughout the Luzon campaign. Pickens was hopeful.

Alas, the mayor turned and simply said, "No one wants to do it."

Pickens spent no time in protesting or entreating. He assembled his patrol for instructions. "Spread out, but stay in sight of the next guy. Protect yourself, but fire only in self-defense. Pass the word when the enemy is sighted. Let's move out."

Hardly two hundred yards into the thicket, Donovan and Rhegetti spotted a clearing where seven Japs were counted. They sat around a fire that must have been used to cook their meal. Their guns were not in sight.

The patrol descended upon them. Yelling and motioning to the enemy soldiers to raise their arms in surrender, the patrol's every gun was trained on what were not prisoners. No shots were fired. Up close, the Americans got a different view of the enemy. They were startled, malnourished, and pitiful, almost bringing about sympathy.

Pickens left Donovan and Rhegetti in charge of the seven while the remainder of the patrol looked for more prisoners. He was clear about his expectations. "I want to count seven when we come back this way. But I also want to find the two of you. Put out of your mind what they would do to you if you were their prisoners. Don't give them an inch, but even this mean, cruel war has rules on how they should be treated. We must obey them."

As the patrol resumed, a new encampment was spotted almost immediately. Blackie passed the word to Pickens. He had counted about thirty Japs.

Pickens, realizing his men were outnumbered, counted on surprise and firepower to capture the enemy. The patrol swooped in, gesturing with raised arms for the Japs to do likewise. One of the enemy reached for his gun. A fusillade of bullets prevented him from doing so. Again, the rest of the captured would ordinarily be sympathetic sights.

The prisoners were confused, but now they were compliant. Pickens and his men gave them no more than the rules allowed. They were always on guard for possible deceit.

Now Pickens lined up the newly-captured for the march through the village and then back to camp. Patrol members walked on either side with guns at the ready, alert for trickery or treachery.

Almost immediately, they came upon the original seven. All were accounted for, and the time had apparently passed without incident. The two groups of prisoners seemed startled at the sight of each other. No words passed between them. They were placed in the line.

The march proceeded anew, if slowly. Oh, so slowly. Victims of dysentery and malnutrition, they were in no condition for speed. The prisoners were a sorry lot as they reached Tacoban.

How the atmosphere of the village had changed since early morning! The once seemingly deserted village was now alive with townspeople. Their understandable hatred for the enemy needed no explanation. The full cruelty of the former captors would be revealed after the war, but enough was known and had been experienced already. The villagers taunted their once proud captors. The patrol members made every effort to prevent physical attack on the now helpless souls. The irony of protecting the enemy from their allies was not lost on the men. They were actually shielding these miserable wretches!

Just as it seemed that the patrol would pass through the village without further incident, it was left to the mayor to provide the most bizarre of incidents. The village leader suddenly emerged in full throttle, hoisting a chair with which he intended to batter one of the now helpless prisoners. As he drew the chair back to deliver a lethal blow, a furious Pickens delivered a blow of his own. His rifle butt struck the mayor in the back before he could deliver his own strike. The mayor was catapulted down a steep ravine, his chair seeming to mock him as it followed in his wake. Pickens cared not for their location or condition.

Pickens was not through with the villagers. "Goddamn it!" he yelled in full throat. "When we came through here this morning, none of you would help us. Not one! Now that we have these poor bastards defenseless, you want to attack them. The war is over. Thank your lucky stars for that. Now keep your hands off our prisoners."

The two-mile trek back to camp had a pace that was snail-like. Defeat had humbled these once proud troops. They had never envisaged being captured. Given the savage nature of the war, they fully expected to be shot. Over and over, they had been told this by their superiors.

When the sorry file entered the company area, the men of the company could only gawk with open mouths. Nary a word was exchanged. Were these the same opponents who they had been fighting so bitterly? Were these the survivors of banzai attacks? Were these really the elite troops?

Rockwell ordered the captives to be marched to the battalion compound. By now some required assistance. The sight of a company soldier aiding his enemy at the end a war marked by untold cruelty seemed incongruous. Tosti would allow that he only did so that the prisoners would be under round-the-clock guard. Perish the thought that he was only helping his fellow man!

Now the talk of the company was the experiences of the Pickens' patrol. Some of the men had figured they had seen it all: mortar barrages, banzai attacks, machine gun fire, and tank assaults. But they had never captured a prisoner. Now they listened.

"It seems so easy now, but the truth is that we were scared the whole time," said Thomas.

"Yeah, and we were outnumbered," added Adronski.

"We were lucky they were in such sad shape," said Holmes.

"They must have been cut off from their outfit," said Lawford.

"I don't think they had any idea that the war was over," Parsons said.

"Actually, protecting them from the Filipinos at Tacoban was the toughest part," said MacElroy. "I thought we were going to have a riot."

"That lick that Pickens laid on the mayor was some belt," drawled Coffey in a way that did not mask his South Carolina roots. "It was a thing of beauty."

Patrols were all part of "mopping up." It sounded so benign, yet men got killed in the process. It also seemed endless. The company had been the first into action in the Pacific. Now it seemed destined to be the last to finish.

It became eerie. By day they had rounded up a group of hapless enemy soldiers. Yet at night they were bracing against attacks that were as fanatical as before. Any company soldier who might have dared to think of what he might do upon his arrival at home had to put his dreams on hold. Mopping up was dangerous.

No attack occurred the night after the patrol. They had been told to expect the worst, but it did not come. No one was disappointed, and no one dared to think that the enemy attacks had ended.

The respite was short-lived. War returned the next night. The enemy seemed intent on making a breakthrough by sheer numbers. Many of them carried no weapons. It was like batting practice for the machine gunners. The attackers charged straight at the guns, giving the appearance of a suicide mission.

The attack ended with a whimper. The enemy body count would take place in the morning. For now it was sobering to report that four in the company had been wounded and Koening had been killed. He had joined the company on the trail. He had seemingly "made it," having survived the war. Alas, he could not survive the mop-up.

"Damn, it's a shame," said Pickens. "His family will never know how close he came."

Now things began to change so rapidly that it defied belief. The most senior of the veterans began to be shipped home. They had survived the diseases, the weather, the perils of the jungle, and the tenacity of the enemy. They had learned how to fight the enemy and schooled others who followed. Now, what seemed interminable ended in a hushed suddenness. The fortunate would board ships for home. It was finally happening.

The squad leaders tried to discuss the newest turn of events. Those who had fought through the nightmare that was New Guinea, the savagery of Leyte, and the ferocity of Luzon had forged relationships that truly defined the meaning of friendship. Now they were as ill at ease as a swain on his first date in determining how they would take leave of one another. Ironically, after overcoming every hurdle on the way to Japan, they would not see their prize. It would be left to those with lesser credentials to occupy Japan. None of the departing expressed any regrets.

Pickens tried to relieve the tension. "I hope those ole boys at home have left me some rabbits to shoot."

Akers wished for no shooting. "The hell with shooting. No more. I hope there's some gals around to date. Just thinking about that is enough to make me willing to swim home."

Kennedy was more sober and reflective. "I can't help but think of guys like Kowalsky, who was squad leader before me. He was such a smart cuss. He knew the fancy words. He would know what to say and do at a time like this."

Akers also turned his thoughts toward others. "We lost so many guys. Some had been here since the early days at Buna. Others had hardly got known. All gone. I hope this is not a waste. I hope that no kid of mine has to go through this goddamned business. No more wars."

Pickens thought of the living. "We were unlucky and lucky at the same time. The best thing that ever happened to us was Captain Leonard. He is the main reason we've survived. What a tough sonofabitch. He's the bravest man I've ever seen."

"Yeah," added Kennedy, "and he's still here. He was wounded four or five times, yet he's always come back for more. What a man!"

Their leave-taking was a blur for all of them. Happy to be going, they knew not how to do it. They contented themselves with slaps on the back, friendly taps at the biceps, and occasional handshakes. They had seen so much of one another. They knew everything about one another. Now they probably would never see one another again. But they didn't know how to say good-bye.

The change in company personnel was stunning. Although Rockwell and some of the New Guinea vets remained, an equal number of the company had never experienced frightening banzai attacks, participated in a patrol, been pinned down by enemy machine gunners, or prayed through mortar shellings. Those who had had these experiences were headed home. That was preferable to Japan.

Meanwhile, back to the war that would seem never to end, things happened swiftly and in ways never anticipated. Leaflets urging Yamashita's surrender that were dropped near his headquarters finally produced the desired results. His response was prompt and conciliatory. In his reply to American commanders, he was unusually civil in tone. Words like "gratitude" and "courteous" reflected the tone. For their part, his American counterparts guaranteed his safety and that of his men.

Captain Leonard, invited to the ceremony, told of it later. "The Americans didn't trust Yamashita to the end. General Beighter refused to shake Yamashita's hand. The old general then stepped back, saluted, and bowed. He was discovering what war was like for losers.

"The old boy was not used to losing, but he knew what losers had to do. He handed over his sword. He tried to stand as straight as his old body would allow. Here was a man who was respected by other military men for his ability to devise and implement strategy. He was the top general in his country. But the rest of the world knew him only as a butcher. Both in China and now in this war, he had presided over terrible cruelties. He will get no mercy. My guess is that he'll be hanged within a year."

Yamashita's surrender had been momentous for another reason. He surrendered 40,000 troops. It was the greatest cache of enemy prisoners during the Pacific War. It seemed incredible. The prisoners showed no sign of relief or joy at having survived the war. They must have thought of the shame in facing families and friends. They would not be greeted as heroes at home.

Now certainly the most eligible for discharge in I Company had a right to think of home and loved ones. The days ahead would be happy ones. The most brutal of wars was truly over. What could possibly stand between them and their return home?

They should have known differently. As always the military had a knack for interfering with what seemed logical. Yes, the war was finally over. But peace for I Company would begin with the occupation of Japan.

Chapter 6

THE OCCUPATION

It gnawed at Rockwell. "Why me? Why am I still here? Why has everyone gone home but me?"

Rockwell's status seemed impossible to explain. According to the "point system" used to determine army discharge, he should have been home in his beloved California long since. He was an original "old timer"—most all of New Guinea, then Leyte and Luzon. With extra points granted for overseas and combat duty, he should have been honing his golf game. Many with lesser service were not aboard the *H. Robert Beasely* as it lurched through the China Sea. Rockwell felt like a stranger in his own company.

Rockwell had had his status explained to him by his superiors, but he was at a loss to explain it to others. It seemed to have something to do with the value of his experience. It left him wondering why the army had allowed so much "experience" to go home. The only rationale that satisfied him was offered by Duggan: "This is the army. Do you expect everything to make sense?"

Rockwell thought of the leave-taking of others. These were men he had fought with, those with whom he had nearly died with, and those whose lives were owed to him. Some of the partings were emotional, but nothing compared with the departure of Captain Leonard.

Much as Rockwell had been around him and as closely he had worked with him in life and death situations, he was always in awe of Leonard. Brave, loyal, fearless: this was Leonard. He was a patriot in the best sense because he demonstrated it. Others might talk of duty, honor, and country. Leonard lived it.

At his leave-taking with Rockwell, Leonard suppressed any emotion that would seem to be unprofessional. He stood ramrod straight. Looking Rockwell straight in the eye, he thanked him for all he had done. He wished him luck and shook his hand in viselike fashion. And then he was gone.

Rockwell's first impulse was to sit down and bawl. Instead, he shouted aloud, "What the hell are they sending him to Fort Benning for?"

The uniqueness of Leonard would make Rockwell chafe at the very thought of taking orders from those who would succeed his beloved captain. Typical of those who fought the war, Rockwell would have difficulty obeying those who did not. What did they know about war? How had they earned their status? Shouldn't they be asking, not telling?

Captain Hudson was the prototype of who and what would easily rankle Rockwell. Fresh out of Advanced Officers' Candidate School, he was eager to place his own stamp on the company. He seemed to radiate efficiency. He talked of enforcing dress codes, drilling, and holding parades. Had he not thought of the difficulties that may lie immediately ahead by occupying a country that doesn't want us? He closed his first meeting with Rockwell aboard ship by saying, "This is still the army. We must never let the men forget that."

Rockwell returned to his quarters in a rage. "We're about to invade a country that dreads our coming and this shave tail is acting like his own men are the enemy. He talks of whipping us into shape. We were in good enough shape to beat the hell out of these birds all over the Southwest Pacific. We didn't do it by drilling and parading. Why didn't they send this guy to Fort Benning and leave Leonard here?"

Johnson tried reason, though he was skeptical of whether it would work. "Look, Manny, admit it. You're not going to be satisfied, no matter who the company commander happens to be. Poor ole Hudson had three strikes against him before he showed up. Looks like his biggest sin was not being around during the war."

Rockwell conceded that he had not been openminded about Hudson. "But he acts as if he knows everything, and we're just a bunch of dopes. Wouldn't you think he'd at least ask someone who has been here a while? Sure, I'm sure that I'm never going to like him. And it looks like he's never going to give me a reason to do so."

Johnson did not respond. Rockwell had at least recognized and acknowledged his bias. Johnson knew that his platoon sergeant had gone about as far as he could go.

Rockwell was more assured by Hudson's daily briefings that followed. He laid out the situation on the ground in Sasebo and the particular mission of I Company. At least Hudson was not totally stupid.

"We're not certain of the reaction we'll get from the Japanese. They don't want us to be here. But we don't expect trouble. And, just in case they cause any kind of trouble, we have all of our guns and ammunition ready. Be careful. Lots of guys are not here because they weren't careful. Remember also that before the surrender, they had intended to do everything and use everyone, even children, to prevent our invasion. So be careful."

Details followed on where they were to be housed and how they should conduct themselves when they met the Japanese. Rockwell noted that the word "Jap" was never used. Now they were "Japanese." He shrugged.

Later meetings dealt with the primary task of the company during the occupation. Hudson was blunt. "We're out to destroy every weapon of war we can find. We want to make it impossible for these guys to wage war again. If we find airplane engines, we'll have to destroy them. If we find ammunition, we'll make them blow it up. No more sneak attacks. No more Pearl Harbors."

The landing was uneventful, but weird. Where were they? There seemed to be no Japanese in sight. Those who were seen were far away, and they quickly scurried for cover.

"I thought Japan was crowded," said Solomon mischievously.

"It must be crowded somewhere else," said Taylor.

Rockwell tried to explain to those within earshot. "Look, it's simple. Their leaders have told their people for years that we were barbarians. Remember that they had to hate us in order to fight us. These people have probably been told that we will slaughter the men and rape the women. It's going to take a lot of convincing for them to think otherwise."

The landing was unusual for other reasons. Sasebo was to have been the invasion site for the I Company. Large loss of life had been expected, as the Japanese had marshaled the entire country to prevent the landing at all cost. Americans had anticipated that another entire invasion force would be needed to establish a beachhead.

Captain Hudson seized the moment to begin the campaign of restoring discipline and order to the company. Men in battle are not judged on their marching in cadence. Most had not paraded since basic training. Hudson would not be deterred. For starters, he personally marched the men to their future headquarters, located two miles from the beach.

The men found the barracks to their liking. Sheets and mattresses had not been a staple at their recent addresses. Being told that these quarters had once housed kamikaze pilots might have been numbing at first, but then came the realization that these suicide pilots had received special treatment. Theirs was no ordinary housing.

Hudson lost no time in getting to the first business of the occupation. He gathered Rockwell and the squad leaders. The latter were largely unknown to Rockwell. Only he remained from the New Guinea fighting. All others were new, as well as Hudson. Rockwell missed his old crew.

Jim Daly had joined the company in the late stages of the Leyte fighting. He was a replacement who had been trained in an anti-tank unit. Like so many of his counterparts, he learned by doing. Though seemingly a typical laid-back Los Angelino, he had been tested and not found wanting on the Villa Verde Trail. Rockwell liked him, if only because he never complained when assigned to lead a patrol.

Allie Stamf had joined the company on the trail. Eager for combat when he arrived, he had been sobered by the ferocity of the fighting and the loss of newly made friends. He had joined the company after only one semester at the University of Wisconsin. He never wavered in dangerous situations and he was respected by his men.

No one was certain why Bill Blackwell had merited squad leader status. At the time, no one seemed to think he had earned it. Most everyone ridiculed the appointment openly. The fact that this had been Hudson's first appointment obviously prejudiced the outlook of the men. Once appointed, Blackwell did gain some grudging acceptance. Eventually, his men would be most upset by his endless eulogies of Ohio State football.

Hudson was eager to take on the intricacies of the occupation, if only to diffuse the fixation on the recently concluded war. Talk of that war served as a constant reminder that he was somehow guilty of not participating in it. Now he had a task he could call his own and, in his mind, it made no difference whether you had been active in the war. That was then. This is now.

Hudson seemed so well prepared for the next meeting it seemed he had been rehearsed. He recited numbers with authority, knowing that no one had the data to refute them. He concentrated on the first task, the destruction of the war materiel. They would be working at a warehouse in the western part of the city, where a mixed cache of these materials existed. In Rockwell's mind, it seemed as if Hudson expected the operation to proceed with clockwork precision. A skeptical Rockwell wondered how yesterday's bitter opponents would so easily become today's willing cooperators. The wily sergeant proved to be right, at least at first.

The first meeting in the warehouse proved to be a mixture of culture clash, misunderstanding, and resentment. The two sides eyed one another with suspicion. The Japanese crew was a motley one, composed of airmen and soldiers of various rank. They had returned home in shame, losers of the war. They had heretofore been regarded as heroes, fighting for the Emperor and the homeland, while now they were reduced to the lowest dregs of society. They resented the mere presence of the enemy on their land. Any diplomatic language like "our loyal Japanese allies" was for the future, not for now.

Under these conditions, preparation for the work began. Rockwell met with the Japanese interpreters to explain what had to be done. As he had anticipated, the process went from slow to static. Rockwell decided to use men from his own company to demonstrate what he wanted his Japanese counterparts to do.

Armed with sledgehammers, Harrington and Rascalli, the two men selected as demonstrators, tore into their task with a vengeance. The objects of their destruction were two airplane engines designed for the infamous Japanese fighter plane known as "Zero." Both of these men had watched in frustration as the highly maneuverable Zeros had often shot the more power-laden American rivals from the sky. Both remembered the inscription of the Japanese rising sun that taunted them from under the wings. Now they took out their exasperation in a demonstration that was without equal.

Rockwell turned to the interpreters. "Now that's what we want your men to do. We must destroy all of the engines, guns, and ammunition connected with war. The best way to make sure that your country can't start a war again is to take away all of your weapons. No more war. Tell your men this over and over. The best way to convince them of that is to have them destroy everything connected with war themselves."

Now it was the interpreters' turn, and they approached their charge with equal animation. They gestured, raised and lowered their voices, and carried on in the best traditions of North Carolina tobacco auctioneers. Each time they stopped, it was only to begin anew. Mercifully, at least for Rockwell and his men, they finally stopped.

Their men sat there, either overwhelmed or unconvinced. They responded slowly, then frequently. It was difficult for the Americans to discern whether they didn't want to begin the destruction of their own weapons or whether they needed further explanation. They seemed to argue with the interpreters, but never among themselves. The interchange threatened never to end.

Rockwell turned to his men. "We've got to be patient. Don't worry. They will destroy those materials. Never fear. Even if it means telling them you will do this or else, they *will* do it."

Whatever was being said in the Japanese interchange, it seemed to Rockwell to be a mixture of confusion and defiance. Were they genuinely confused? Did they understand the consequences of defiance? Told until the very end of the war they were winning the war, were they still not convinced of their defeat?

Hudson had discussed with Rockwell both the precision he wanted and the timetable he expected. He need acknowledge the need for patience, the confusion that might result, and the ultimatums that might be necessary. But while Hudson expected initial difficulty, he never recognized the extent of the problem. Although he preached that the war was over, Hudson was to begrudgingly learn that participation in it would have afforded him a better understanding of the opposition. That, rather than Officers' Candidate School, would have been a better teacher on this score.

The first day was approaching late afternoon. The precision expected by those in offices far removed from reality was not being met. Rockwell had demonstrated uncharacteristic patience, but in so doing, not a single plane engine had been destroyed by the Japanese.

His patience exhausted, Rockwell ordered the interpreters to meet with him. It was clear that he was in no mood for discussion or dialogue. Now it was he who waved his arms and raised his voice.

"I don't care what your men feel. I don't give a damn about their opinions. They need to know they are being ordered to do something. Do they really understand that they lost the war? They are not being mistreated. The lies their leaders told them of how we would mistreat them was done to keep them fighting. Who cares now whether or not they like what they're supposed to do?

"Tell your men this. Tomorrow they will begin the day by destroying these engines. We are through talking. Remember my men are getting damned impatient. Who knows how long I can control them? We won't have another day like this. Talk is over. Action will begin. We'll see you tomorrow."

What went on and what did not go on was the subject of intense discussion when the men returned to the barracks. "Can you believe these guys? Of all the nerve," began Epstein.

"They simply must be confused," interrupted Balboni. "Remember that the past weeks must have been a shocker to them. They'd been told for years that they were winning the war. All of a sudden the Emperor surrenders. Huh?"

"Know? Hell, they know," replied a frustrated Dunstan. "They know all right. They just hope to draw things out so we will give up on the project."

Alverez was probably closest to the truth. "I think the problem is with the officers, especially the fly guys. Just as in our case, these guys are the glamour boys. They think they are better than everyone else. Give them a bomber jacket and they become obnoxious. The thought of going from special treatment to taking orders from the enemy has got to be too much."

The next day was eagerly anticipated by the I Company men. Would they or wouldn't they? And what if they wouldn't?

Rockwell left nothing to chance. He reminded the interpreters of what he had reminded them a day ago. No fooling, no delaying, no protesting: that was the formula. So let us begin.

The initial Japanese efforts were not so robust or spirited as their American counterparts had demonstrated. However, working through the interpreters, the I Company men did encourage and receive a more intense Japanese effort. The work proceeded with an ebb and flow that produced some periods of slowdown. Each time Rockwell or one of his men interceded with effect. The engines were being destroyed and the pile that was amassing in the warehouse would never have been mistaken for any modern sculpture.

The days following saw identical results. Once the supply of plane engines was depleted, the destruction proceeded anew, now involving mortars, machine guns, and small arms. The process worked so well that Rockwell could turn his attention elsewhere.

Together with Daly's squad, Rockwell turned his attention to the harbor at Sasebo. What they found there was more than interesting; it was chilling. Guns on the high ground overlooking the harbor were trained on the area where any invasion would take place. They were mounted on hydraulic lifts that could be raised or lowered, thus shielding them from damage from the air. Any potential landing here seemed suicidal in retrospect. And this is where I Company's role in Olympic was to be played out!

The men of I Company had known that they were to be in the second wave of the invasion. They also knew that the prediction was that a third wave would be needed to gain a solid beachhead. Looking through the magnified lenses of the guns, McNamara uttered a steady stream of words best left unprinted. In polite parlance, it amounted to "shooting fish in a barrel."

The day's events were topics for discussion upon return to the barracks. The guns remained on their minds.

Blackwell began it. "You may think I'm crazy, but I'm glad I was sent over here, if only to see the guns. It makes me want to thank who-ever dropped those big bombs and ended the war."

"Yeah," Petrey went on. "Some of the old hands who have already gone home should have been with us today. They would have realized how close we came to a disaster."

"And when you realize that their women and children were going to blow themselves up in order to do as much damage as possible to us...," said MacKenzie. "Lots of us would never have survived this."

McLean toyed with heresy when he said, "Maybe we should stop bitching and be thankful. What we complain about is peanuts compared to how lucky we were."

McLean was looked upon as from another planet. Imagine no chance to bitch!

Meanwhile, Rockwell reported his findings at the harbor to Hudson. There was no conjecture between them as to what had to be done. Clearly, any destruction of the guns there was a task for something more than sledgehammers. Drilling and dynamiting would be required. It was also no assignment for amateurs. A demolition team with special expertise would have to be called upon. The guns had to be destroyed.

Rockwell had been so occupied that he hadn't realized that the occupiers had settled into some sort of routine. By day the concentra-tion was on overseeing the elimination of the weapons of war. Alas, late afternoons featured a much-reviled parade once a week, and at least one drill to prepare for it. By now Rockwell could tolerate what he considered to be foolish because he knew that each day passed was one day closer to his discharge. He would indulge in no disobedience that would delay his leave-taking.

Rockwell also realized that this was the best duty that he had known. He no longer was subjected to the monsoons of New Guinea, the mud of Leyte, or the mountains of Luzon. Imagine sleeping in dry quarters nightly; isn't this what they had dreamed about? By night, movies were available. Cigarettes were provided by the carton. Japanese beer, begrudgingly good, came in gallons. Food was good, but it was not fashionable to say so.

Day passes were available for travel to select places. Still skeptical of what reaction they would receive from the Japanese, the men were transported in truck convoys and traveled in groups at their destination. There had been no untoward incidents to date.

Rockwell's first foray elsewhere was to Fukuoka, north of Sasebo, and considered to be the cultural capital of Kyushu. The American presence there was not as great as Sasebo. However, fear of the war-time enemy was giving way to a curiosity about the occupiers. Direct contact with the Americans was still avoided, if possible. Shopkeepers were the exception. Desperate for sales, they managed to transact business with the I Company men by a weird combination of hand signals, contorting body language, and the occasional recognition of basic words in one another's language. Business was brisk, and smiles abounded.

The nip in the autumn air reminded some of fall at home. The sky was painter's blue and picture book clear. The Japanese bowed on their way by, averting eye contact and traveling at great speed. Rockwell was enjoying his first experience among those once considered the enemy. He was having a great visit.

Suddenly, the peace of the noonday was noisily interrupted. People began racing wildly down the streets, shouting in unintelligible Japanese as they sped in the direction of the men. Rockwell froze. Had he and his men been lured into a trap? Was this an attack?

Rockwell had not to fear. The crowd raced past and more came in their wake. What made them run? What did they fear? How could he find out?

Fortunately, he began to hear occasional words of English. "Hurry up!" was most common. "Let's stop the next guy we hear speaking English," yelled Rockwell above the din.

"Here's one over here," shouted Simpson. The men braced themselves as they poised to stop the runner. In stopping his momentum, they were almost driven to the ground.

The "captured" man was petrified. He feared the worst of what he had been told by his authorities. Rockwell gave him little time for any more worry. "Why is everybody running?" he asked.

The man paused long enough to catch his breath. He pointed to the sky. "B-29," he screeched, over and over. Then, as quickly as he was stopped, he was gone.

The Americans looked skyward. Sure enough, high in the clear-blue sky, a lone plane glistened in the sunlight. It was a B-29. The brutal memories of war remained alive, but no bombs would be dropped.

Back at camp, Rockwell prepared for more demolition work. It was not to be. Instead, he was notified to report to Hudson's headquarters at 08:00 hours on the next day. There were no further details. He tried hard to recall anything that would have made him subject to reprimand. On the other hand, he could think of no reason for commendation. What then? He worried all night.

Rockwell saluted smartly as he was ushered into Hudson's office. The latter, army-like to the core, began immediately.

"Rockwell, I realize your time over here was not always pleasant. You've felt from the beginning that you should have been sent home long ago. All of your fellow old hands have been gone long since. You have resented those of us who saw little or no front line action, despite the fact that we all take orders and go where we are sent.

"You may be surprised to hear this, but I'm glad that you were kept on. We never would have the company so well acclimated without your leadership. For that you have my thanks.

"And lastly, your orders came through yesterday. Get your gear in order. A truck convoy will be here at 08:00 hours tomorrow to take you to a staging area in Nagoya. Your ship will leave soon after that."

The two men stood. They exchanged salutes. "Good luck," offered Hudson. Rockwell made his about face and left.

Rockwell returned to his quarters, but his mind was a blur. The men were gone. Who was leading them? For the first time in over three years, he was without his company. He was not indispensable. The company could and would get along without him. It was humbling.

The joy and the anticipation of going home overcame any nostalgic feelings. He thought of old girlfriends and old buddies at home. Good-bye to parades, to discipline and orders, to pre-dawn risings, and to "Kilroy Was Here" graffiti. Most of all, good-bye to foxholes, killing, monsoons, and banzai attacks. Good-bye to war, which already seemed long ago. Would anyone give a damn about all this someday?

The trip to Nagoya involved army truck, then train, then truck again. The trucks were not built with comfort in mind. No one cared. Each mile they logged was one closer to home. The mood of the men was one of relief, rather than celebratory. At the Nagoya staging area, they were to be housed in yet another barracks. Rockwell staked out a bunk. He wasn't fussy. He was headed home.

Things moved swiftly. Rockwell's ship would leave tomorrow. It was the *Robert S. Hughes*. Who the hell cared?

Rockwell and his fellow would-be passengers were marched to the docks in the murky dawn. They lined up at the gangplank of the ship. And, typical of army protocol, they waited.

A Japanese band provided the music of departure. They played the hit song of the day, "Sentimental Journey." Rockwell sung the words to himself, "Going to take a sentimental journey…sentimental journey home." The band was awful, but no one cared. The idea was wonderful.

Rockwell began his ascent on the gangplank, his heavy duffel bag never seeming lighter. At the top of the plank he paused to look back. He tried to think of some memorable thing to say, or some grandiose gesture to make. What would MacArthur do or say? Or even John Wayne?

He had been to all of those unknown and soon to be forgotten places. He had had so many men under his responsibility. Some returned home unscathed, some returned with scars, and some returned only to cemeteries. He had performed heroic deeds and won his share of medals. Some men owed their lives to him.

He was a citizen-soldier, one who had done his duty and served his country in its greatest hour of peril. Now he relished a return to his status as citizen. So many places, so many skirmishes, so many brushes with death. Yet he could think of none of them or pronounce any words for the ages. He merely gulped. And then the tears.

"C'mon, let's move it," came the shout from below. "You're holding up the whole damn line."

Rockwell turned to board the ship. He was headed home.

THE AUTHOR

A three-year infantryman of I Company of the 127th Regiment of the 32nd Division, Henry C. Zabierek received a bachelor's degree at the University of Rhode Island, a master's degree from Boston University, and a doctorate degree at Carnegie Mellon University. As an educator for forty-six years, both as a teacher and administrator, he has written chapters for books and articles for local and national publications. Zabierek was one of the co-authors of the original text of "Facing History and Ourselves," a curriculum on the Holocaust that is now used for over a million and a half students throughout the world. The program has been featured on national television shows hosted by Bill Moyers and on the *Today* show. When he passed away in 2008 at the age of 84, he left behind only two living members of I Company.

OF RELATED INTEREST

AMERICAN WARRIORS
Five Presidents in the Pacific Theater of World War II
Duane T. Hove

Five United States presidents—Johnson, Kennedy, Nixon, Ford, and George H. W. Bush—served their country as Naval Reserve officers in the Pacific Theater of WWII. This book reconstructs the presidents' wartime roles based on interviews with more than one hundred veterans and on primary sources such as action reports, ships' logs, war diaries, and letters.

ISBN 978-1-57249-307-0 • Hardcover $24.95

ANOTHER SIDE OF WORLD WAR II
A Coast Guard Lieutenant in the South Pacific
Juliana Fern Patten

Lt. Fern's warm and personable letters, spanning two years at sea in the South Pacific, offer an alternative view of life aboard ship during World War II. Seizing every opportunity for an adventure, he muses upon his assignment living at sea and its inherent challenges. His varied duties aboard three different ships afford Fern numerous vantage points regarding his unique war experiences.

ISBN 978-1-57249-377-3 • Softcover $14.95

HAWAII GOES TO WAR
The Aftermath of Pearl Harbor
Wilbur D. Jones Jr. & Carroll Robbins Jones

For six months following the December 7, 1941, attack on Pearl Harbor, Hawaii rearmed and awaited the inevitable. Patricia O'Meara Robbins, a professional photographer, documented everyday life as the shocked Oahu community recovered from one attack and prepared for another.

ISBN 978-1-57249-260-8 • Softcover $14.95

WHITE MANE PUBLISHING CO., INC.

To Request a Catalog Please Write to:
WHITE MANE PUBLISHING COMPANY, INC.
P.O. Box 708 • Shippensburg, PA 17257
e-mail: marketing@whitemane.com
Cover design by Angela Guyer

Breinigsville, PA USA
05 August 2010
243085BV00003B/4/P